FINDING THE GRASSROOTS

A Directory of New York City Activist Organizations

First Edition

North Star Fund

FOREWORD

The North Star Fund is a progressive, public foundation that funds projects in New York City organized by the people most affected and oppressed by current economic, social, and political problems. We support grassroots groups that actively educate and organize in their communities to create a more just and equitable society.

Founded in 1979, North Star is a unique partnership of community activists and donors dedicated to building a permanent institutional and financial base for progressive social change.

North Star raises its budget each year through large and small contributions. Since its inception, North Star has awarded millions of dollars to more than 1,000 community-based organizations. Given the tremendous challenges New York City communities are facing in these difficult times, North Star's resources are needed more than ever.

North Star's funding decisions are made by a Community Funding Board of activists who reflect the range of issues and constituencies that we support. In addition to grantmaking, North Star also sponsors technical assistance workshops, forums, and conferences for activists and donors. For additional information about North Star and how you can help support our work, please call our office.

This new *Finding the Grassroots: A Directory of New York City Activist Organizations* is consistent with North Star's goal of not only providing financial resources, but also promoting the networking, skills sharing, and collaborative work of community groups. This Directory is also created in response to needs expressed by participants at North Star's 1993 city-wide conference, "Organizing for Social Change: Fighting Racism & the Politics of Division." With listings of over 300 community-based groups, this is an important resource for organizations who are mobilizing and organizing around the crucial issues that affect all our lives.

We hope this directory is helpful. Put it to good use, and we welcome your comments.

North Star Fund
October, 1995

INTRODUCTION

This directory is a resource for individuals and organizations who support progressive social change and who want to connect with others who share this perspective. The groups listed cover a wide range of issue areas and constituencies. The goal of this directory is to help New York City activists and organizers find each other, increase networking, and decrease isolation.

This is the first edition of the directory; undoubtedly, many organizations that should be listed are omitted. If you know of groups that you think should be included, please let us know; we will periodically update listings.

HOW TO USE THIS DIRECTORY

The Directory's Organization

The directory is organized **alphabetically** by the name of the organization. An **Index** of all organizations listed begins on **page 214.** Following the alphabetical index are two others. The second is an index of organizations by **issue and constituency areas.** For example, if you are interested in looking up organizations that engage in anti-violence work, you would turn to this index and check each of the organizations listed on the page numbers following the heading "Anti-Violence." If you are interested in organizations whose work is targeted to Asian/Pacific Islander communities or to lesbians or gay men, you would look under the headings "Asian/Pacific Islander" or "Lesbian/Gay." The last index is by **geographic scope.** This index will help you find groups that work in your borough or your neighborhood. It will let you know which groups organize statewide and which are national or national affiliates.

The descriptions were provided by the organizations themselves, although we have edited for clarity, conciseness and consistency. Each organization was asked the same set of questions so that information given would be as uniform as possible. As you will see, the listings range from organizations that have full-time staff and office hours to organizations staffed by volunteers that may only be reachable evenings or weekends.

Not For English Speakers Only

The Directory is primarily in English. However, we asked each organization to tell us whether it was multi-lingual and we asked organizations to translate their entry if they worked with a bi-lingual or multi-lingual membership or clientele. (When an entry says Bilingual: Spanish, the second unlisted language is English. Each of the organizations in the directory has the ability to communicate in English.) Our goal has been to indicate to Directory users who only speak Spanish or Chinese, for example, whether they would be able to call a particular organization and communicate in their language. The organizations listed in the sections entitled **Spanish-Speaking Organizations, Chinese-Speaking Organizations**, etc. are only those who indicated that they operated bilingually or multi-lingually in all areas of their work, e.g., answering the phone, meetings, and materials.

- See listings in Spanish, beginning on page 169.
- See listings in French, beginning on page 202.
- See listings in Creole on page 205.
- See listings in Chinese, beginning on page 206.
- See listings in Korean, beginning on page 211.

ACKNOWLEDGMENTS

This Directory was made possible through the participation of hundreds of community organizations. The North Star Fund thanks all of you for helping us create this Directory and we thank you for the important and vital work you do every day. We would like to particularly thank the following organizations who generously provided us with their mailing lists of organizations: **Center for Constitutional Rights**, *City Limits*, **Committee Against Anti-Asian Violence**, and the **Educational Center for Community Organizing**.

This Directory was prepared, designed and produced, with the extensive assistance of consultant **Susan Hibbard** and her staff associate **Dora Mendez**. We thank Susan and Dora for their commitment, dedication, and brilliance.

We thank the **Health & Hospital Workers Union Local 1199** for their great generosity in printing this Directory. Their support makes it possible to provide this publication to community groups at low cost. Many thanks to **Red Hook Arts** for the use of the cover photograph and to **David Cloyce Smith** for his cover design and layout assistance. Thanks to **Roberto Lugo** for the photograph from the 1993 conference.

We thank the following individuals who participated in the translations, computer technology and production of the Directory: **Cora Acebron, Manuel Molina, Celeste Douglas, Lauri Cohen** and **Marc Lapidus**.

Many thanks to the anonymous donors who provided critical financial support. Thank you for sharing North Star's mission to support progressive social change.

CONTENTS

Part 1:

..........Activist Organizations
Alphabetical Order

A.C.E.-OUT, INC.

103 East 125th Street, Suite 602
New York, NY 10035

Phone: 212-289-0538
Fax: 212-289-1057
Contact: Antionettea Etienne, Exec.
           Director

Office Hours: 9am-6pm
Staff: Paid and volunteer
Geographic Scope: City-wide

Organizational Focus:
A.C.E.-Out, Inc. is organized by and
for female ex-offenders who are
infected with or affected by
HIV/AIDS.

General Description:
We assist women in transition from
city and state correctional facilities.
We provide case management, buddy
programs, peer counseling and
outreach to the community.

Bi-lingual: Spanish

Organizational Resources: Speakers'
bureau and meeting space.
Regular Public Meetings: No
Membership Organization?: No

Issues:	Constituencies:
HIV/AIDS	Multi-Racial
Women's Rights	Women

A.J. MUSTE MEMORIAL INSTITUTE

339 Lafayette Street
New York, NY 10012

Phone: 212-533-4335
Contact: Murray Rosenblith,
           Executive Director

Office Hours: Mon.-Fri. 9am-5pm
Staff: Paid
Geographic Scope: National

Organizational Focus:
To explore and teach how
nonviolence can be used to bring
about world peace, as well as social
and economic justice.

General Description:
Through grants, sponsorships, the
publication *Social Change Resources*,
and the development of independent
educational programs, we seek to
further the goals of prominent US
pacifist A.J. Muste and promote
nonviolence for social change.

Bi-lingual: Publish some literature in
Spanish

Organizational Resources:
A quarterly newsletter, grants,
literature on nonviolence (catalogue
available), office space for social
change groups occasionally becomes
available in the building.
Membership organization?: No

Issues:
Peace/
Anti-Militarism
Social Justice
Anti-Violence

ACT UP

135 West 29th Street, 10th Fl.
New York, NY 10001

Phone: 212-564-2437
Fax: 212-594-5441
Contact: Walt Wilder, Workspace
Manager

Office?: Yes
Staff: None
Geographic Scope: City-wide

Organizational Focus:
ACT UP focuses on finding ways to stop AIDS through many means including public demonstrations, phone, letter and fax zaps.

General Description:
ACT UP is a diverse direct action non-partisan collection of individuals united by anger and committed to direct action in order to end the AIDS crisis.

Organizational Resources: Newsletter and the member-power to apply pressure on politicians and bureaucrats who stand in the way of resolving the AIDS crisis.
Regular Public Meetings: Mondays at 7:30pm, at the Lesbian & Gay Community Center, 208 W. 13th St.
Membership Organization?: No

Issues: Constituencies:
HIV/AIDS   All affected by
Gov't Accountability   HIV/AIDS
Social Justice   Lesbian/Gay
                            Multi-Racial

ACTION FOR COMMUNITY EMPOWERMENT (ACE)

126 West 119th Street
New York, NY 10026

Phone: 212-932-3324
Fax: 212-923-3973
Contact: Rima McCoy, Director

Office Hours: 10am - 6pm
Staff: Paid and volunteer
Geographic Scope: Central Harlem

Organizational Focus:
Organizes tenants of city-owned buildings to fight for improved services and repairs; involves neighborhood youth in responding to community problems.

General Description:
ACE brings people together on projects to develop leadership, promote critical consciousness and improve the quality of life. Members have demanded repairs and basic services in HPD buildings by conducting pickets, marches and public meetings. ACE members are converting a lot into a garden.

Organizational Resources: Newsletter and presentations/workshops on organizing around poverty, homelessness and housing.
Membership Organization?: Yes
Membership Requirements: $10/Year dues and attend meetings

Issues: Constituencies:
Housing/   African American
Homelessness   Youth
Social Justice   Women
Gov't Accountability
Leadership Development

ADVOCATES FOR CHILDREN OF NEW YORK, INC. (AFC)

24-16 Bridge Plaza South
Long Island City, NY 11101

Phone: 718-729-8866
Fax: 718-729-8931
Contact:: Galen D. Kirkland, Exec.
          Director

Office Hours: 9am - 5pm
Staff: Paid
Geographic Scope: City-wide

Organizational Focus:
Organized in 1970 to ensure free, equal and quality educational services for NYC's 1,000,000 public school students.

General Description:
AFC represents individual parents and children in administrative hearings and education-related meetings; trains parents and youth advocates in education, law and advocacy; performs limited class action litigation on issues affecting at-risk children.

Multi-lingual: Spanish, Chinese, French

Organizational Resources: Newsletter, pamphlets, publications, and a parent trainer.
Membership Organization?: No

Issues: Constituencies:
Education   NYC public
Students   school students
Legal

AFRICAN-AMERICAN PARENT COUNCIL, INC.

185 Parkhill Avenue, #LB
Staten Island, NY 10304

Phone: 718-876-9195
Fax: 718-448-5875
Contact: Minnie Graham, Exec.Dir.

Office Hours: By appointment
Staff: Volunteer
Geographic Scope: North Shore of Staten Island

Organizational Focus:
To encourage minority parent involvement and advocate on behalf of minority parents and children for improvements in S.I. North Shore schools.

General Description:
To provide a variety of services and programs to the at-risk minority population of Staten Island's North Shore.

Membership Organization?: No

Issues: Constituencies:
Youth   African-American
Anti-Violence   Caribbean
Education   Latino/Hispanic
HIV/AIDS   Women
                  Youth

AFRICAN PEOPLES CHRISTIAN ORGANIZATION

415 Atlantic Avenue
Brooklyn, NY 11217

Phone: 718-596-1991
Fax: 718-625-3410
Contact: Bro. Leroy Applin, Exec.
            Director

Office Hours: 9am - 5pm
Staff: Volunteer
Geographic Scope: City-wide

Organizational Focus:
African nation-building

General Description:
APCO struggles for human rights and
self-determination for all, while trying
to build an African Christian nation.
To this end, we pool and expand our
skills, talents and resources. We
engage in education and mobilization.

Organizational Resources: News-
letter, APCO Timbuktu Learning
Center, lecture series, broadcasts,
research division, college division
Regular Public Meetings: Yes
Membership Organization?: Yes
Membership Requirements: People of
African descent

Issues:	Constituencies:
Social Justice	African American
	Caribbean
	Latino/Hispanic
	Native American

AFRIKAN FREE SCHOOL

PO Box 485, Lincolnton Sta.
New York, NY 10037

Phone: 212-606-3719
Contact: Eric Jennings, Exec. Dir.

Office?:   No
Staff: Volunteer
Geographic Scope: City-wide

Organizational Focus:
To recreate the extended family by
establishing bonds between the
parents, staff, students and the
community for the education of
young minds.

General Description:
The group operates a 13-week fall
and spring semester, 1-day a week
school. Classes Afrikan American
history, Literature/Language Arts and
Math. In addition to academics the
Afrikan Free School Inc. offers
swimming, computers, chess and a
free lunch.

Organizational Resources:
Workshop facilitators, meeting space
for special events.
Membership Organization?: Yes
Membership Requirements:
Registration and orientation

Issues:	Constituencies:
Education	Youth 5-14
Parental/Community	African American
involvement	Latino/Hispanic
Anti-Racism	Low income
African American culture	

AIDS COMMUNITY TELEVISION (DIVA TV)

12 Wooster Street
New York, NY 10013

Phone: 212-226-8147
Fax: 212-966-5622
Contact: James Wentzy, Producer

Office Hours: 10am-7pm
Staff: Volunteer
Geographic Scope: City-wide

Organizational Focus:
AIDS Community Television is a weekly television series to energize the fight against AIDS.

General Description:
AIDS Community TV documents AIDS activism; advocates for issues of underserved communities; educates the public; furthers coalition-building between increasingly diverse and specialized community organizations; and motivates involvement and action in the fight to end AIDS.

Organizational Resources:
Videos/programming of weekly series can be seen on Manhattan Cable on Tuesdays at 11pm, Channel 69 (repeated Fridays at 9am) & in all boroughs on CUNY TV, Channel 75, first Wednesday of the month at 10:30am, 3:30 & 8:30pm & 12:30am.
Membership Organization?: No

Issues:
HIV/AIDS
Media
Gov't Accountability
Education
Social Justice

Constituencies:
Multi-Racial
Lesbian/Gay
Anyone affected by HIV/AIDS

AIDS SERVICE CENTER

80 Fifth Avenue, Suite 405
New York, NY 10011

Phone: 212-645-0875
Fax: 212-645-0705
Contact: Gregory Rice, Director of Programs

Office Hours: 9am-5pm
Staff: Paid
Geographic Scope: Manhattan, 59th Street to 96th Street area

General Description:
Founded in 1990, ASC initially emerged from the Lower Manhattan AIDS Task Force, a local consortium of concerned health and social service providers who mobilized to obtain funding in order to create an agency to identify community needs, develop strategy to respond to service gaps, and improve access to critical services. ASC is now a multi-service community organization that also engages in advocacy.

Bi-lingual: Spanish

Organizational Resources: Pamphlets, volunteer training, stipend program.
Regular public meetings: Monthly
Membership Organization?:No

Issues:
HIV/AIDS
Health Care
Education

Constituencies:
Multi-Racial

ALIANZA DOMINICANA, INC.

2410 Amsterdam Avenue, 4th Fl.
New York, NY 10033

Phone: 212-740-1960
Fax: 212-740-1967
Contact: Milgros Baptista, Program
          Director

Office Hours: 9am-5pm
Staff: Paid
Geographic Scope: Washington
Heights, Manhattan

Organizational Focus:
To help children, youth, and families
break the vicious cycle of poverty
and fulfill their potential as members
of the community.

General Description:
Alianza has many programs including:
the only drug treatment program for
crack and cocaine addicts in
Washington Heights and the only
community-based drug treatment
service; an AIDS rap group, a mental
health project, an immigration
program and a school-based
community center.

Bi-lingual: Spanish

Organizational Resources: Newsletter and pamphlets as well as the
programs and services we provide.
Regular Public Meetings: Yes
Membership Organization?: No

Issues: Constituencies:
Drug Rehabilitation   Latino/Hispanic
Housing/Homelessness
Education
Human Rights
Econ. Development

ALLIANCE FOR THE ARTS

330 West 42nd Street, Rm. 1701
New York, NY 10036

Phone: 212-947-6340
Fax: 212-947-6416
Contact: Patricia Hegemo, Deputy
          Director

Office Hours: 9:30am - 5:30pm
Staff: Paid and volunteer
Geographic Scope: City-wide

Organizational Focus:
The Alliance For The Arts is a non-
profit organization dedicated to
policy research, information services
and advocacy for the arts in New
York.

General Description:
The Alliance acts on behalf of the
non-profit arts community as a cata-
lyst for change and new thinking. We
gather information about culture
which is useful to funders and
members of the community.

Organizational Resources: Pamphlets
like: *Future Safe: Estate Planning for
Artists with AIDS, Kids Culture
Calendar, Kids Culture Catalog, NYC
Culture Catalog* and *The Arts as an
Industry.*
Membership Organization?: No

Issues: Constituencies:
Arts/Culture   Multi-Racial
Lesbian/Gay   Lesbian/Gay
                     Youth

ALLIANCE FOR THE MENTALLY ILL OF NYS

432 Park Ave. South #710
New York, NY 10001

Phone: 212-684-3264
Fax: 212-684-3364
Contact: Ronald Nieberding, Dir.

Office Hours: 10am-6pm
Staff: Paid and volunteer
Geographic Scope: City-wide

Organizational Focus:
AMI/FAMI supports, educates, and comforts those who suffer or have family members suffering from schizophrenia, manic or major depression. AMI/FAMI increases public awareness and advocates for more research and improved service.

General Description:
AMI/FAMI is a non-profit, self help, volunteer organization comprised of over 900 family members and friends of people who suffer from neuro-biological disorders, as well as people who suffer from NBDs themselves.

Organizational Resources: News-letter, help line, support groups, speakers, resource center, factsheets.
Regular Public Meetings: 2nd Wednesday of month
Membership Organization?: Yes
Membership Requirements:
$20/Person $25 Family

Issues: Constituencies:
Mental Illness   Mentally ill &
Disability Rights   their families
Health Care
Gov't Accountability
Housing/Homelessness

ALONZO DAUGHTRY FAMILY LIFE SERVICES

415 Atlantic Avenue
Brooklyn, NY 11217

Phone: 718-596-3454
Fax: 718-625-3410
Contact: Leah Daughtry, Exec.
           Director

Office Hours: 9:30am - 5:30pm
Staff: Paid and volunteer
Geographic Scope: City-wide

Organizational Focus:
Advocacy and social services for people in need in communities of color.

General Description:
ADFLS takes a holistic approach to service: identifying the needs of people in the community it serves and aggressively developing and utilizing both traditional and innovative ways to address and advocate for these needs.

Organizational Resources: Meeting space, speakers' bureaus, workshop facilitators and panelists.
Regular Public Meetings: Tuesday evenings at 7pm.
Membership Organization?: No

Issues: Constituencies:
Social Service   African American
Personal   Caribbean
Empowerment   Women
                     Youth

AMANAKA'A AMAZON NETWORK

584 Broadway, Room 814
New York, NY 10012

Phone: 212-925-5299
Fax: 212-925-7743
Contact: Zeze Weiss, President

Office Hours: 10am - 6pm
Staff: Paid and volunteer
Geographic Scope: City-wide

Organizational Focus:
Amazon rain forest and its peoples.

General Description:
Dedicated to educating the American
public about the Amazon rain forest
and its peoples.

Multi-lingual: Portuguese, Spanish,
French

Organizational Resources: News-
letter, videos, workshop facilitators,
and meeting space.
Regular Public Meetings: Amazon
Week every spring
Membership Organization?: Yes
Membership Requirements: Dues
$25/Yr. or $35 for 2 years

Issues: Constituencies:
Environment   Native Peoples
Education
Human Rights

AMERICAN COMMITTEE ON AFRICA

17 John Street, 12th Floor
New York, NY 10038

Phone: 212-962-1210
Fax: 212-964-8570
Contact: Jennifer Davis, Exec. Dir.

Office Hours: 10am-6pm
Staff: Paid
Geographic Scope: City-wide

Organizational Focus:
Advocating a US policy that supports
political and economic justice in
Southern Africa.

General Description:
Since 1966, the Africa Fund has
supported the struggle for African
freedom by educating Americans and
supporting grassroots organizations
that point the way towards a new
Southern Africa.

Organizational Resources: Newsletter, pamphlets, literature, videos
Membership Organization?: No

Issues:
International Solidarity
Women's Rights
Econ. Development

AMERICAN FRIENDS SERVICE COMMITTEE -- NY
Metropolitan Regional Office
15 Rutherford Place
New York, NY 10003

Phone: 212-598-0950
Fax: 212-529-4603
Contact: Lisa North, Institutional Fundraiser

Office Hours: 9:00am-5:00pm
Staff: Paid and volunteer

Organizational Focus:
Conflict resolution, criminal justice and immigrants' rights.

General Description:
The AFSC is a Quaker organization which includes people of various faiths who are committed to social justice, peace and humanitarian service. Its work is based on the Quaker belief in the worth of every person and faith in the power of love to overcome violence and injustice.

Bi-lingual: Spanish

Membership Organization?: No

Issues:	Constituencies:
Conflict Resolution	African American
Immigrants' Rights	Latino/Hispanic
Youth	Youth
Crime/Criminal Justice	

AMERICAN INDIAN COMMUNITY HOUSE
404 Lafayette Street, 2nd Floor
New York, NY 10003

Phone: 212-598-0100
Fax: 212-598-4909
Contact: Curtis Harris, Dir, HIV/ AIDS Project

Office Hours: 9am-6pm
Staff: Paid
Geographic Scope: City-wide

General Description:
To provide HIV prevention, education and case management to Native Americans in NYC and to develop and maintain a regional network of Native American HIV service providers.

Organizational Resources: Newsletter, educational materials
Regular Public Meetings: At least twice a month
Membership Organization?: Yes
Membership Requirements: Native American

Issues:	Constituencies:
HIV/AIDS	Native American
Arts/Culture	Lesbian/Gay
Health Care	
Legal	
Anti-Racism	

AMERICAN SOCIAL HISTORY PRODUCTIONS

99 Hudson Street, 3rd Floor
New York, NY 10013

Phone: 212-966-4248
Contact: Stephen Brier, President

Office?: Yes
Staff: Paid
Geographic Scope: City-wide

Organizational Focus:
The development of new media in support of the work of public school and college teachers and community and labor organizers. Advocate for education reform and for a change in the way social studies is taught.

General Description:
ASHP is committed to producing educationally sound and progressive videos and other media that aid organizers and teachers in giving voice to US working people in the past and present.

Membership Organization?: No

Issues:
Education
Media
Workers' Rights
Multiculturalism
Social History

AMERICAN-ARAB ANTI-DISCRIMINATION COMMITTEE (ADC)

PO Box 435
New York, NY 10185

Phone: 212-642-8454

Office?: No
Staff: None
Geographic Scope: City-wide

General Description:
ADC was founded to defend the rights of people of Arab descent and to promote their rich ethnic heritage.

Bi-lingual: Arabic

Organizational Resources: Newsletter and pamphlets on anti-discrimination.
Membership Organization?: Yes
Membership Requirements: Dues: $35/Yr. to national

Issues: Constituencies:
Anti-Racism   Palestinian/
Media   Middle Eastern
Arts/Culture
Legal

ART WITHOUT WALLS

100 Clearmont Avenue
Brooklyn, NY 11205

Phone: 718-237-0762
Fax: 718-237-0762
Contact: Mae Jackson, Exec. Dir.

Office Hours: 9am-3pm
Staff: Paid
Geographic Scope: City-wide

Organizational Focus:
Children of incarcerated mothers

General Description:
Provide counseling, after-school
centers, S.A.T. preparation and
career counseling. We also provide
transportation for children and
extended family members of
incarcerated mothers.

Organizational Resources: Speakers
and transportation.
Membership Organization?: No

Issues:	Constituencies:
Arts/Culture	African American
Crime/Criminal	Multi-Racial
Justice	Youth
Education	Women
Youth	

ARTISTS RESPONSE TO

5 East 16th Street, 7th Fl.
New York, NY 10003

Phone: 212-255-4177
Fax: 212-727-8563
Contact: Hope Sandrow, Exec.
            Director

Office Hours: Staff is part-time
Staff: Volunteer
Geographic Scope: City-wide

Organizational Focus:
AHC is an innovative public art project in which artists and arts professional create art together with the
homeless in NYC shelters.

General Description:
AHC provides volunteer-run art
workshops at various shelters. AHC
collaborates with various organiza-
tions, including: Food and Hunger
Hotline, Whitney Museum, Henry St.
Settlement, Visual AIDS, WAC, and
MOMA.

Membership Organization?: No

Issues:	Constituencies:
Housing/	Women
Homelessness	Youth
Arts/Culture	
Education	
Women's Rights	
Youth	

ASIAN AMERICAN ARTS ALLIANCE

339 Lafayette Street
New York, NY 10012

Phone: 212-979-6734
Fax: 212-979-8472
Contact: Christine Lipat, Programs
          Manager

Office Hours: Mon.-Fri. 11-5pm
Staff: Paid and volunteer
Geographic Scope: City-wide

Organizational Focus:
Asian American Arts Alliance is dedicated to increasing the support, recognition, and appreciation of Asian American arts.

General Description:
Arts Alliance activities focus on information, networking, and advocacy services.

Organizational Resources: Monthly Asian American arts calendar, quarterly newsletter *Dialogue*, resources and opportunities listings, and a directory of Asian American arts organizations. Information referral and resource library of Asian American literature, files on arts organizations and individuals, and journals (open to public but borrowing privileges for paid members.)
Membership Organization? Yes
Membership Requirements:
Community membership

Issues:	Constituencies:
Arts/Culture	Asian/Pacific Islanders

ASIAN AMERICAN ARTS CENTRE

26 Bowery Street, 3rd Fl.
New York, NY 10013

Phone: 212-233-2154
Fax: 212-766-1287
Contact: Robert Lee, Exec. Dir.

Office Hours: Gallery 11am-6pm
Staff: Paid and volunteer
Geographic Scope: City-wide

Organizational Focus:
The Asian American Arts Centre focuses on Asian and Asian American arts and culture.

General Description:
AAAC is a non-profit organization founded in 1974. Its programs include: exhibitions and research on visual arts, folk arts documentation and presentation, arts in education, AAA slide archive, and dance presentations.

Organizational Resources: Newsletter, bulletin board of events and activities, educational program, gallery tours, pamphlets, videos, artist slide archive, referrals, our publication *Artspiral*, and a meeting space.
Membership Organization?: No

Issues:	Constituencies:
Arts/Culture	Chinatown
Education	community
	Asian/Pacific Islanders
	Multi-Racial
	Youth

ASIAN/AMERICAN CENTER, QUEENS COLLEGE

65-30 Kissena Blvd.
Flushing, NY 11367

Phone: 718-997-3050
Fax: 718-997-3055

Office Hours: 9am-5pm
Staff: Paid
Geographic Scope: City-wide

Organizational Focus:
Community-oriented research on Asian groups; intercultural relations; bridging gaps between scholarship and activism.

General Description:
The Asian American Center at Queens College of CUNY is dedicated to the development of community-oriented research to analyze the multicultural Diaspora experience of Asians in North, Central, and South America and the Caribbean.

Multi-lingual: Chinese, Hindu and Korean

Organizational Resources:
Newsletter
Regular Public Meetings: Yes
Membership Organization?: No

Issues:	Constituencies:
Education	Asian/Pacific
Arts/Culture	Islanders
Anti-Violence	Multi-Racial
Anti-Racism	Students
Social Justice	Asian Diaspora

ASIAN AMERICAN FEDERATION OF NEW YORK (AAF)

95 Madison Avenue, #1309
New York, NY 10016

Phone: 212-725-3840
Fax: 212-725-6629
Contact: Cao O, Exec. Director

Office Hours: Mon.-Fri. 9am-5pm
Staff: Paid
Geographic Scope: City-wide

Organizational Focus:
AAF's mission is to galvanize leadership and resources in support of community efforts to improve the quality of life of Asian Americans.

General Description:
AAF is a not-for-profit membership organization of health and human service agencies that address the needs of the New York City Asian American community.

Multi-lingual: Chinese, Korean, Vietnamese

Organizational Resources: Newsletter, meeting space for members (non-members on case by case basis), data on Asian Americans, workshops, and a resource library. The literature is in English only.
Membership Organization?: Yes
Membership Requirements:
501(C)(3) Organizations

Issues:	Constituencies:
Human Services	Asian/Pacific
Voting Rights	Islanders
Senior	Seniors

ASIAN AMERICAN LEGAL DEFENSE & EDUCATION FUND

99 Hudson Street, 12th Floor
New York, NY 10013

Phone: 212-966-5932
Fax: 212-966-4303
Contact: Margaret Fung, Exec. Dir.

Office Hours: 9:30am-5:30pm
Staff: Paid
Geographic Scope: City-wide

Organizational Focus:
Legal/Civil Rights

General Description:
AALDEF does litigation, legal advocacy and community education for Asian American communities in the areas of immigrants' rights, anti-Asian violence, labor rights, voting rights, Japanese American redress and environmental justice.

Multi-lingual: Chinese, Korean, Japanese

Organizational Resources: Pamphlets, legislative alerts, and speakers
Membership Organization?: Yes
Membership Requirements: Support AALDEF's principles and goals

Issues:	Constituencies:
Legal	Asian/Pacific
Social Justice	Islanders
Voting Rights	
Workers' Rights	
Immigrants' Rights	

ASIAN AMERICAN UNION FOR POLITICAL ACTION

PO Box 1102 Knickerbocker Sta.
New York, NY 10002

Phone: 718-857-2849
Contact: Mini Liu, Chair

Office?: No
Staff: None
Geographic Scope: City-wide

Organizational Focus:
Policies affecting working class and poor Asian Americans' ability to develop stable, economically-viable communities with decent jobs.

General Description:
We are Asian American activists, labor organizers and community workers. We have organized campaigns to preserve manufacturing jobs on the lower east side, to consolidate working class community power in electoral redistricting, and to defend the rights of immigrant workers.

Newsletter?: Yes
Membership Organization?: Yes
Membership Requirements: Support AAUPA's political perspective

Issues:	Constituencies:
Anti-Racism	Asian/Pacific
Social Justice	Islanders
Econ. Development	
Workers' Rights	

ASIAN AMERICAN WRITERS' WORKSHOP

296 Elizabeth Street, 2nd Floor
New York, NY 10012

Phone: 212-228-6718
Contact: Curtis Chin, Managing Dir.
Office?:   Yes

Office Hours: N/A
Staff: Paid and volunteer
Geographic Scope: City-wide

General Description:
The AAWW was founded to provide
a space for Asian American writers
to meet and nurture their artistic
voices. We program events that give
artists and readers an opportunity to
discover Asian American literature.

Regular Public Meetings: Call for
specific information.
Membership Organization?: Yes
Membership Requirements: Interest
in supporting Asian American
literature.

Issues:	Constituencies:
Arts/Culture	Asian/Pacific
Media	Islanders
Lesbian/Gay	Multi-Racial
Women's Rights	
Human Rights	

ASIAN AMERICANS FOR EQUALITY, INC.

111 Division Street
New York, NY 10002

Phone: 212-964-2288
Fax: 212-964-6003
Contact: Scott Ito, Exec. Assistant

Office Hours: 9am - 5pm
Staff: Paid
Geographic Scope: Chinatown/
Lower East Side

Organizational Focus:
Low income housing development
and management, economic development, food distribution, citizenship
classes, youth leadership training and
other services to seniors and
immigrants.

General Description:
AAFE focuses on protecting and
promoting the rights of Asian Americans, other people of color and all
those in need, in the areas of civil
rights, affordable housing, economic
development, and social services.

Multi-lingual: Chinese (Mandarin &
Cantonese)

Organizational Resources: Newsletter, bi-lingual counselor and staff
Membership Organization?: Yes
Membership Requirements: Dues
$20 & $10/Student

Issues:	Constituencies:
Housing	Asian/Pacific
Anti-Racism	Islanders
Youth	Seniors
Immigrants' Rights	Multi-Racial
Econ. Development	Jewish
Social Justice	

ASIAN AND PACIFIC ISLANDER COALITION ON HIV/AIDS, INC.

275 7th Ave. 12th Floor
New York, NY 10001

Phone: 212-620-7287 Voice/TTY
Fax: 212-620-7323
Contact: John Manzon, Exec. Dir.

Office Hours: Mon.-Fri. 10am-6pm
Staff: Paid
Geographic Scope: City-wide

Organizational Focus:
APICHA provides HIV/AIDS prevention education and HIV/AIDS-related client services targeted to Asians and Pacific Islanders in the NYC area.

General Description:
APICHA's programs target women, young people, and gay and bisexual men. APICHA trains volunteers and peer educators, provides technical assistance, limited case management, and arranges for language interpreters. APICHA coordinates, support groups for Asian and Pacific Islanders living with HIV/AIDS, friends/family/lovers of people with HIV/AIDS, and gay/bisexual A&PI men "coming out".

Multi-lingual: Cantonese, Hindi, Tagalog, Visayan and American Sign Language.

Organizational Resources: Newsletter, multi-lingual educational brochures, workshops on HIV/AIDS and A&PIs, and cultural sensitivity trainings.
Membership Organization?: No

Issues: Constituencies:
HIV/AIDS   Asian/Pacific
                     Islanders

ASSOCIATED BLACK CHARITIES (ABC)

105 East 22 Street, Suite 915
New York, NY 10010

Phone: 212-777-6060
Fax: 212-777-7904
Contact: Barbara L. Edwards, Exec.
           Director

Office Hours: Mon.-Fri. 9am-5pm
Staff: Paid
Geographic Scope: City-wide

Organizational Focus:
Financial assistance, technical assistance, and public policy advocacy for ABC human service organizations.

General Description:
ABC is a not-for-profit federation of health and human service organizations that are located throughout the five boroughs of New York City. Our membership includes agencies that provide daycare, foster care, counseling and preventive services.

Organizational Resources: Newsletter, meeting space, speakers' bureau, workshop facilitators, and technical assistance support.
Regular Public Meetings: Yes, yearly
Membership Organization?: Yes
Membership Requirements: Member agencies must provide direct human services to NYC's Black community.

Issues: Constituencies:
Community Dev.   African American
Social Justice   Caribbean
Health Care   Latino/Hispanic
Gov't Accountability Multi-Racial
Econ. Development

ASSOCIATION FOR NEIGHBORHOOD & HOUSING DEVELOPMENT

305 Seventh Ave. Suite 2001
New York, NY 10001

Phone: 212-463-9600
Fax: 212-463-9609
Contact: Jay Small, Exec. Director
Office Hours: Mon.-Fri. 9am-5pm
Staff: Paid
Geographic Scope: City-wide

Organizational Focus:
Our mission is to promote polices and programs to meet the housing needs of New York City's low income population.

General Description:
Within that framework, we provide advocacy, policy analysis, technical assistance, training and research services as well as publications to our membership and their constituencies. We have over 70 member community based organizations from all of New York City.

Organizational Resources:
ANHD Weekly Reader, publication, trainings, newsletter
Regular Public Meetings: Bimonthly
Membership Organization?: Yes
Membership Requirements: Locally-based non-profit

Issues: Constituencies:
Housing/   Multi-Racial
Homelessness   Low income
Social Justice   NYC communities

ASSOCIATION FOR UNION DEMOCRACY

500 State Street, 2nd Floor
Brooklyn, NY 11217

Phone: 718-855-6650
Fax: 718-855-6799
Contact: Herman Benson

Office Hours: 9:30am-5:30pm
Staff: Paid
Geographic Scope: City-wide

Organizational Focus:
Democratic rights for workers in their unions and on the job.

General Description:
As a pro-union organization, AUD educates union members about their rights and about how to organize to enforce them.

Organizational Resources:
Newsletter
Membership Organization?: Yes
Membership Requirements: $25/yr.

Issues: Constituencies:
Workers' Rights   Multi-Racial

ASSOCIATION FOR UNION DEMOCRACY MINORITY WORKERS RIGHTS PROJECT

508 State Street
Brooklyn, NY 11217

Phone: 718-855-6650
Fax: 718-855-6779
Contact: Herman Benson, Secretary
            Treasurer

Office Hours: 10am-4pm
Staff: Paid and Volunteer
Geographic Scope: City-wide

Organizational Focus:
For equal rights in unions and on the job.

General Description:
Aim to help organize self-governing groups of workers to campaign for civil rights and civil liberties in their unions and on the job.

Bi-lingual: Spanish speaking aides

Organizational Resources: Pamphlets, brochures, publications and classes for unionists.

Issues:	Constituencies:
Workers' Rights	Multi-Racial
Social Justice	Latino/Hispanic
Anti-Racism	Women
Human Rights	

ASSOCIATION OF HISPANIC ARTS, INC. (AHA)

173 East 116 Street, 2nd Floor
New York, NY 10029

Phone: 212-860-5445
Fax: 212-427-2787
Contact: Sandra Perez, Director of
            Programs

Office Hours: Mon.-Fri. 9:30-5:30
Staff: Paid
Geographic Scope: City-wide

Organizational Focus:
To serve Latino/a artists and Latino arts organizations through technical assistance, advocacy, information services, publications, etc.

General Description:
Founded in 1975, AHA is a not-for-profit service organization dedicated to advancement of Latino arts, artists and arts organizations. Promote wealth of Latino arts and culture to Latino and non-Latino audiences through programs and services designed for this purpose.

Bi-lingual: Spanish

Membership Organization?: No

Issues:	Constituencies:
Arts/Culture	Latino/Hispanic

ATURA COALITION

PO Box 170610
Brooklyn, NY 11217

Phone: 718-643-9603
Contact: Ted Glick, Chairperson

Office Hours: 9am-6pm
Staff: None
Geographic Scope: Brooklyn

Organizational Focus:
Working for community
development at Atlantic Terminal
Urban Renewal ATURA site.

General Description:
We advocate and organize for low
and moderate income housing, jobs, a
youth recreation and education
center and environmentally sound
development at the ATURA site.

Organizational Resources: Speakers
Regular Public Meetings: Monthly
Membership Organization?: Yes
Membership Requirements: Come to
meetings and be active.

Issues:
Community Development
Econ. Development
Housing/Homelessness
Environment

BEDFORD PARK STREET TREE GUARDIANS

219 Bedford Park Blvd.
Bronx, NY 10458

Phone: 718-933-1377
Contact: Mariana T. Morera,
           Founder

Office?:   No
Staff: None
Geographic Scope: Bedford Park,
the Bronx

Organizational Focus:
Neighborhood quality of life

General Description:
To protect and maintain the street
trees in the neighborhood and solve
any problem that may occur in the
neighborhood re: lights, traffic,
sanitation, police, etc.

Bi-lingual: Spanish

Membership Organization?: No

Issues:
Environment

BETANCES HEALTH UNIT

281 East Broadway
New York, NY 10002

Phone: 212-227-8408
Fax: 212-227-8842
Contact: Raul Guevarez, Comm.
               Relations

Office Hours: 9am-5pm
Staff: Paid
Geographic Scope: Lower East Side,
Brooklyn-Williamsburg

Organizational Focus:
Primary care facility, with additional
services including podiatry, nutrition
and prenatal care.

General Description:
25 year old non-profit community
health center that offers alternative
therapies like acupuncture, massage
therapy, nutrition, HIV/AIDS early
intervention and accepts all forms of
payment, including the uninsured on
a sliding fee basis.

Multi-lingual: Spanish and Chinese

Organizational Resources: Pamphlets,
videos, workshops.
Membership Organization?: No
Regular Public Meetings: Yes, health
education workshops at public
schools

Issues: Constituencies:
Health Care   Latino/Hispanic
HIV/AIDS   Asian/Pacific
                          Islander
                          African American
                          Jewish

BEYOND SHELTER COALITION

150 West 96th Street, #5E
New York, NY 10025

Phone: 212-865-6647
Contact: Henry Freedman,

Office?:   No
Staff: Paid
Geographic Scope: Upper West
Side

Organizational Focus:
Representing Jewish community of
Upper West Side of Manhattan in the
struggle for affordable housing for
the homeless.

General Description:
Coalition of synagogues and religious
institutions working together in education, advocacy and support of a
loan fund to promote permanent
housing for homeless persons.

Membership Organization?: No

Issues: Constituencies:
Housing/   Jewish
Homelessness

BLACK STUDENT LEADERSHIP NETWORK -- NY METRO CHAPTER

1251 Dean Street, 4th Floor
Brooklyn, NY 11216

Phone: 718-771-3042
Fax: 718-398-8972
Contact: Dorothy Chavannes, Co-
           Chair

Office Hours: By appointment
Staff: Volunteer
Geographic Scope: City-wide and national

General Description:
The Black Student Leadership Network is a national organization of Black college students and young community-based activists committed to improving the conditions of Black children and youth through effective community service and advocacy. The New York Metro Chapter was organized to launch a local student/young adult movement on behalf of youth.

Organizational Resources: We are currently developing a student leadership training series to begin in the fall of 1995.
Membership Organization?: No

Issues:	Constituencies:
Student	African American
Youth	Caribbean
	Latino/Hispanic
	College students
	Youth

BLACKBERRY PRODUCTIONS

250 West 54th Street, Suite 800
New York, NY 10019

Phone: 212-586-3700
Fax: 212-348-2848
Contact: Stephanie Berry, Artistic
           Director

Office: None
Staff: Volunteer
Geographic Scope: City-wide

Organizational Focus:
To develop original theater for community facilities and the theater arena that speaks to political issues.

General Description:
Blackberry Productions is a community-based theater company that has a dual purpose: to create original theater and build a repertory company and to develop Arts-in-Education programming to reach our youth.

Organizational Resources: Annual newsletter, Arts-in-Education workshops, teacher or community leader training in using the arts to empower people.
Regular Public Meetings?: No
Membership Organization?: Yes
Membership Requirements:
Attending workshops

Issues:	Constituencies:
Arts/Culture	African-American
Education	Caribbean
Youth	Latino/Hispanic
	Youth
	Seniors
	Multi-Racial

BLACK VETERANS FOR SOCIAL JUSTICE

686 Fulton Street
Brooklyn, NY 11217

Phone: 718-935-1116
Fax: 718-935-1629
Contact: Steve Williams, Deputy
           Director

Office Hours: 9am-6pm
Staff: Volunteer
Geographic Scope: City-wide

Organizational Focus:
Providing entitlement and social
services assistance to veterans and
their families.

General Description:
We provide veterans with information to help alleviate some of their
problems. We advocate to federal,
state, and city agencies to meet the
immediate needs of vets and to
develop long-range solutions. We
attempt to provide both care and
redress.

Bi-lingual: Spanish (some staff)

Organizational Resources: Speakers,
pamphlets, workshops and videos,
employment and skills training,
referrals and job placement, legal
assistance, counseling and housing
assistance
Regular Public Meetings: Yes
Membership Organization?: Yes

Issues: Constituencies:
Veterans' rights   Veterans
readjustment
Housing/Homelessness
Peace/Anti-Militarism

BODY POSITIVE

2095 Broadway, Suite 306
New York, NY 10023

Phone: 212-721-1618
Fax: 212-787-9633
Contact: Jeffrey Karaban, Dir. of
           Support Services

Office Hours: Mon.-Fri. 9am-6pm
Staff: Paid and volunteer
Geographic Scope: City-wide

Organizational Focus:
Helping people when they first learn
they or a loved one is HIV positive.

General Description:
Support groups, educational programs, social activities, outreach,
hotline, volunteerism and a monthly
magazine for HIV positive people and
their friends and families.

Bi-lingual: Some programs in Spanish

Organizational Resources: Newsletter, speakers, print materials
Regular Public Meetings: Yes
throughout city, listed in magazine
Membership Organization?: No

Issues: Constituencies:
HIV/AIDS   Anyone affected
                     by HIV/AIDS

BREAD AND ROSES CULTURAL PROJECT, INC.

330 West 42nd Street, 15 Fl.
New York, NY 10036

Phone: 212-631-4565
Fax: 212-695-0538
Contact: Moe Foner, Exec. Dir.

Office Hours: 9am-5pm
Staff: Paid and volunteer
Geographic Scope: City-wide

Organizational Focus:
Bread and Roses, the cultural arm of 1199, the health care workers' union, arranges programs in the arts and humanities for a predominantly women of color membership.

General Description:
Bread and Roses produces theater, music programs, exhibitions, original musical revues, conferences, videos, books, and posters.

Bi-lingual: Spanish

Organizational Resources: Posters, teaching guides, book, videos, cassettes. *Women Of Hope: African Americans Who Made A Difference*, a 12-poster set and teaching guide. Preparing *Latina Women Of Hope. Images of Labor,* a 10 set poster series. We have brochures describing these materials.
Membership Organization?: No

Issues: Constituencies:
Arts/Culture   Multi-Racial
Education   African American
Workers' Rights Latino/Hispanic
Anti-Racism
Women's Rights

BREAK BREAD ... FOR A CHANGE

118 Remsen Street
Brooklyn, NY 11201

Phone: 718-797-4175
Fax: Same/Call first
Contact: Tony White, Outreach
         Coordinator

Office Hours: Mon.-Fri. 9am-5pm
Staff: Volunteer
Geographic Scope: City-wide

Organizational Focus:
We organize a monthly potluck meeting featuring an interesting speaker and vegan (pure vegetarian) food. Presentations address issues concerning ecology, health, compassion and sustainability.

General Description:
By gathering together to break bread and network, we nourish our spirit, re-energize our commitment, stimulate our interest and develop our resources.

Organizational Resources:
A monthly potluck, on the 4th Tuesday of the month, at which people can pick up plenty of information sheets. We also produce a quarterly mailing announcing speakers.
Regular Public Meetings: 4th Tuesday of month
Membership Organization?: No

Issues:
Sutainability
Anti-Violence
Health Care
Environment

THE BRECHT FORUM

122 West 27th Street, 10th Floor
New York, NY 1000-6281

Phone: 212-242-4201
Fax: 212-741-4563
Contact: Liz Mestres, Director

Office Hours: 1:30-8:30pm
Staff: Paid and volunteer
Geographic Scope: Citywide

Organizational Focus:
The Brecht Forum works to provide
educational and cultural resources to
help strengthen left and progressive
culture through study, analysis,
discussion and exchange of ideas and
experiences.

General Description:
The Brecht Forum is an educational/
cultural institution where people
working for a new culture that puts
human need first can meet, study
together and analyze social reality
and ways of changing it.

Bi-lingual: Spanish

Organizational Resources: Our
program is conceived of as a
resource, but we also rent meeting
space at low cost to many
organizations. We refer speakers
and, on occasion, mailing lists to
targeted constituencies.
Regular Public Meetings: Yes,
evenings and weekends on a regular,
ongoing basis

BRONX LESBIAN AIDS TASK FORCE

PO Box 1738
Bronx, NY 10451

Phone: 718-829-9817
Fax: 718-731-2885
Contact: Lisa Winters, Co-Founder

Office?:   No
Staff: None
Geographic Scope: Bronx

Organizational Focus:
HIV/AIDS resource provision

General Description:
Network of HIV positive lesbians and
women advocates working to create
services for lesbians living with
HIV/AIDS in the Bronx. Also provide
lesbian and AIDS agency-based
trainings, and peer education groups.

Multi-lingual: Spanish

Organizational Resources:
Speakers' bureau, workshop facilita-
tors.
Regular Public Meetings: 3rd Friday of
month, 9:30-11:30am
Membership Organization?: No

Issues:	Constituencies:
HIV/AIDS	HIV+ & HIV
Lesbian/Gay	affected
	Multi-Racial
	Lesbian/Gay

BRONX LESBIANS UNITED IN SISTERHOOD (BLUES)

PO Box 1738
Bronx, NY 10451

Phone: 718-330-9196
Contact: Lisa Winters, Founder

Office?: No
Staff: None
Geographic Scope: City-wide

Organizational Focus:
Educational and social multicultural lesbian organization. The only lesbian organization in the Bronx. Empowerment through sisterhood.

General Description:
Multi-cultural membership organization dedicated to addressing the social and political needs of the Bronx lesbian community.

Bi-lingual: Spanish

Organizational Resources:
Information about lesbian specific activities in the Bronx and provide extensive referrals.
Regular Public Meetings: 2nd Tues. of month
Membership Organization?: Yes
Membership Requirements: $15 annual dues

Issues:	Constituencies:
Lesbian/Gay	Lesbians
Anti-Racism	Multi-Cultural
Women's Rights	
Education	

BRONX SECOND CHANCE

900 Sheridan Avenue
Bronx, NY 10451

Phone: 718-590-3448
Contact: Carmen Sabedra, Program Director

Office Hours: 8:30am-2pm
Staff: Volunteer
Geographic Scope: Bronx

Organizational Focus:
Bronx Second Chance provides educational and psychological services that foster intellectual and emotional development. Its aim is to reduce the rate of recidivism and court petition for adults.

General Description:
The staff is all volunteer including the Executive Director and the program is open to people of all ages. First time misdemeanor offenders receive an A.C.D. also alternative to incarceration. All must perform a community service. All types of counseling available.

Multi-lingual: Spanish and Italian

Membership Organization?: Yes
Membership Requirements: Interest in working to better the lives of multi-racial adults and youthful offenders.

Issues:	Constituencies:
Crime/	Multi-Racial
Criminal Justice	
Anti-Racism	
Youth	

BRONX HOMELESS TASK FORCE

920 Sherman Ave. (163rd Street)
Bronx, NY 10451

Phone: 718-588-6790
Contact: Marshall England, Ex. Dir.

Office Hours: 9am-9pm
Staff: Volunteer and paid
Geographic Scope: City-wide

General Description:
We organize, counsel, provide services, job referrals, GED and college preparation and general advocacy including direct interaction with elected officials and administrative appointees on behalf of homeless people. We also engage in homeless litigation primarily on living conditions within NYC's shelters or residences. We provide full time Merchant Mart "Bargain Village" through which we teach business skills.

Organizational Resources:
Newsletter, meeting space, and workshop facilitators.
Regular Public Meetings?: Organizing school and Bronx health forum weekly. In addition, the Homeless Task Force regularly coordinates sessions with residents of neighboring shelters.
Membership Organization?: Yes
Membership Requirements: An interest in our goal and projects

Issues:
Anti-Racism
Econ. Development
Health Care
Housing/
Homelessness

Constituencies:
Multi-Racial
Seniors
Women
Youth

BRONX VOTER PARTICIPATION PROJECT

2432 Grand Concourse, Rm. 504
Bronx, NY 10458

Phone: 718-365-5071
Fax: 718-584-3258
Contact: Nina Laboy, Director

Office Hours: 9am-5pm
Staff: Paid
Geographic Scope: South Bronx

Organizational Focus:
Non-partisan voter registration, education, election turnout and community empowerment.

General Description:
We are a project of the Community Service Society of New York. The project believes that through an increased understanding of how the political system works and by developing organizing skills low income residents can fight effectively for better government representation and improved city services.

Bi-lingual: Spanish

Organizational Resources:
Voting rights information workshops and forums, meeting space, technical assistance, coalition-building, and community organizing.
Membership Organization?: No

Issues:
Voting Rights
Gov't. Accountability
Education
Social Justice

Constituencies:
Multi-Racial

BROOKLYN CHINESE-AMERICAN ASSOCIATION

5002 8th Avenue
Brooklyn, NY 11220

Phone: 718-438-9312
Fax: 718-438-8303
Contact: Paul Mak, President/CEO

Office Hours: Mon.-Fri. 9am-5pm
Staff: Paid
Geographic Scope: Serving the
Chinese-American community in
Sunset Park, Boro Park, and Bay
Ridge.

Organizational Focus:
Community services

General Description:
We provide social services such as: a
program for mentally retarded and
developmentally disabled people;
employment and skills training,
including ESL classes; a family day
care network; a confidential police
infoline; cultural and recreational
activities for seniors, and a day care
center.

Bi-lingual: Chinese

Organizational Resources: ESL
classes, information hotline, an annual
Chinese New Year celebration
parade, summer street fairs, and an
annual summer day camp.
Membership Organization?: No

Issues: Constituencies:
Health Care   Seniors
Education   Youth
Econ. Development Women
Gov't Accountability Disabled People
Welfare Advocacy Asian/Pacific
                        Islanders

BROOKLYN PARENTS FOR PEACE

304 A Henry Street, Suite 1458
Brooklyn, NY 11201

Phone: 718 624-5921
Contact: Charlotte Phillips, Chair

Office?: No
Staff: None
Geographic Scope: Brooklyn

Organizational Focus:
Network of parents concerned about
militarism and violence in society.

General Description:
Brooklyn Parents For Peace is primarily educational, providing
resources to parents. We are
involved in action campaigns, letter-
writing, telephone calls and public
meetings.

Organizational Resources: Books,
some video resources for workshops, particularly for concerns
about militarism and violence in
society and culture and effects on
children.
Membership Organization?: Yes
Membership Requirements: Willingness to participate; having one's
own children is not a requirement.

Issues: Constituencies:
Peace/   Parents
Anti-Militarism
Social Justice
Anti-Violence
Anti-Racism

CAMBRIA HEIGHTS REAP & KEEP SERVICES

227-12 Linden Blvd.
Cambria Heights, NY 11411

Phone: 718-528-0608
Contact: Dr. Daisy King, Exec.
Director

Office Hours: 9:00am-5:00pm
Staff: Volunteer
Geographic Scope: Queens

Organizational Focus:
The less affluent segment of the Cambria Heights community and its surrounding environs.

General Description:
Reap and Keep provides services: after school homework assistance, high school equivalency preparation, parental support, substance abuse prevention/recovery, and summer day camp.

Organizational Resources:
Newsletter
Membership Organization?: No

Issues:
Education
Youth
Anti-Violence
Women's Rights
Crime/Criminal Justice

CAMP KINDERLAND

1 Union Square West
New York, NY 10003
Summer Address:
1543 Colebrook River Road
Tolland, MA 01034

Phone: 212-255-6283 winter
413-258-4463 summer
Contact: Alice Grunfeld, Director

Staff: Paid
Geographic Scope: City-wide

Organizational Focus:
Children's summer camp.

General Description:
Full sports, swimming, arts, trips and campcrafts activities; in a community setting that promotes progressive, secular Jewish and multi-cultural values of peace, social justice, anti-racism, and human rights struggle on behalf of women, workers, gays/lesbians, etc. Partial scholarships available.

Organizational Resources:
Newsletter, camp is available off season(spring, late summer, fall) for very reasonable rental for conferences, retreats, encampments.

Issues: Constituencies:
Youth   Youth

CAMPAIGN FOR A NEW TOMORROW (CNT)

PO Box 520103
Flushing, NY 11352

Phone: 718-898-3753
Contact: Mary France, NYS
           Coordinator
Office?:   No
Staff: Volunteer
Geographic Scope: National

Organizational Focus:
Independent political party

General Description:
CNT is a nationwide, independent, progressive political organization led by people of African descent and other people of color whose goal is to build a grassroots, independent political party, having the interests of oppressed groups, working people, and the poor as its core political agenda.

Organizational Resources: Newsletter and pamphlets
Membership Organization?: Yes
Membership Requirements: $15 annual dues; $10 for students, low income or unemployed people and seniors.

Issues: Constituencies:
Gov't Accountability Multi-Racial
Human Rights
Social Justice

CAMPAIGN FOR PEACE AND DEMOCRACY

PO Box 1640, Cathedral Station
New York, NY 10025

Phone: 212-666-5924
Fax: 212-662-5892
Contact: Joanne Landy, Exec.
           Director

Office Hours: 9:30am-5:30pm
Staff: Paid
Geographic Scope: City-wide

Organizational Focus:
CPD is dedicated to promoting a new, progressive and democratic US foreign policy.

General Description:
CPD publishes a magazine "Peace And Democracy," organizes conferences, public forums, seminars, and demonstrations.

Organizational Resources: Videos, speakers, and a magazine.
Regular Public Meetings: Occasional
Membership Organization?: No

Issues:
Human Rights
Peace/Anti-Militarism
Social Justice
Women's Rights
Workers' Rights

CAMPAIGN FOR REAL EQUITABLE ECONOMIC DEVELOPMENT (CREED)

c/o NSN
338 Lafayette Street, #8
New York, NY 10012

Phone: 212-645-5230
Fax: 212-645-7280

Office: No
Staff: Volunteer
Geographic Scope: City-wide

Organizational Focus:
Education, pressure and solidarity among social movements in the US and abroad in support of real development alternatives to "neoliberal" economic programs.

General Description:
Coalition of New York area groups working in solidarity with Latin America and the Caribbean. Works on campaigns to build local grassroots support for alternatives to the "neoliberal" policies (such as austerity, privatization, NAFTA, GATT) the US government is imposing on developing countries.

Multi-lingual: Creole, Portuguese and Spanish
Membership Organization?:No

Issues:
Int'l Solidarity
Social Justice

CARIBBEAN LESBIAN AND GAY ORGANIZATION

c/o 100 S. Oxford
Brooklyn, NY 11217

Phone: 212-614-6482
Fax: 212-614-6499
Contact: Suzanne Shende, Member

Office?:   No
Staff: None
Geographic Scope: City-wide

Organizational Focus:
Newly forming political and social organization of Caribbean lesbians and gay men, bisexuals and transgender.

General Description:
We are committed to working for political change and social justice and affirming our identities as Caribbean lesbians and gays. We work against racism, homophobia, sexism, class oppression and other inequities, and we celebrate our community.

Organizational Resources:
Speakers and information packets. We plan to create videos and pamphlets.
Regular Public Meetings: First and third Thursday of month, 7pm at 85 S. Oxford, Brooklyn, Lafayette Presbyterian Church
Membership Organization?: No

Issues: Constituencies:
Social Justice   Lesbian/Gay
Anti-Racism   Caribbean
Lesbian/Gay
Women's Rights
Immigrants' Rights

THE CENTER FOR ANTI VIOLENCE EDUCATION/ BROOKLYN WOMEN'S MARTIAL ARTS

421 5th Avenue
Brooklyn, NY 11215

Phone: 718-788-1775
Fax: 718-369-3192
Contact: Brenda Jones,
          Administrative Director

Office Hours: Mon.-Fri. 12-6pm
Staff: Paid
Geographic Scope: City-wide

Organizational Focus:
Educational programs training
violence prevention and self defense
with feminist and anti-racist
perspective.

General Description:
The Center/BWMA is a feminist and
anti-racist organization, founded in
1974, teaching violence prevention
and self defense through courses at
its site in Park Slope, Brooklyn and
workshops for organizations and
groups all over the NYC area.

Organizational Resources: We offer
workshops in self defense and
violence prevention
Membership Organization?: No

Issues: Constituencies:
Women's Rights   Women
Anti-Violence   Multi-Racial
Youth   Youth
Social Justice   Lesbian

CENTER FOR CONSTITUTIONAL RIGHTS (CCR)

666 Broadway, 7th Floor
New York, NY 10012

Phone: 212-614-6464
Fax: 212-614-6499
Contact: Ron Daniels, Exec. Dir.

Office Hours: 9:30am-5:30pm
Staff: Paid
Geographic Scope: National

General Description:
CCR is a non-profit legal and
educational organization dedicated to
advancing and protecting the rights
guaranteed by the US Constitution
and the Universal Declaration of
Human Rights.

Organizational Resources: News-
letter, pamphlets, brochures, hotline
(Break the Contract on America).
Regular Public Meetings: Sporadically
Membership Organization?: No

Issues: Constituencies:
Legal   Multi-Racial
Education   Women
                     Lesbian/Gay
                     Low-income
                     people

CENTER FOR IMMIGRANTS' RIGHTS, INC. (CIR)

48 St. Marks Place
New York, NY 10003

Phone: 212-505-6890
Fax: 212-995-5876
Contact: Franklin Velazquez, Acting Executive Director

Office Hours: Mon.-Fri. 9:30-5:30
Staff: Paid
Geographic Scope: City-wide

Organizational Focus:
CIR was founded to protect and expand the rights of immigrants, regardless of legal status.

General Description:
Immigrants are assisted and empowered through community organizing, education, policy, advocacy and legal services. CIR also provides information, referral, counseling and advocacy through its telephone hotline service on immigration, employment and public benefit rights.

Multi-lingual: Spanish, French, Cantonese, Mandarin

Organizational Resources:
Fact sheets on workers, public benefits and immigration rights; trainings for CBO's and workshops to immigrant audiences; and, a hotline.
Membership Organization?: Yes
Membership Requirements: $35 Dues

Issues: Constituencies:
Immigrants' Rights   Multi-Racial
Human Rights
Legal

CENTER FOR INDEPENDENCE FOR DISABLED IN NY

841 Broadway, 2nd Fl.
New York, NY 10003

Phone: 212-674-2300
Fax: 212-254-5953
Contact: Marilyn Saviola, Executive Director

Office?: Yes
Staff: Paid
Geographic Scope: Manhattan

Organizational Focus:
To integrate people with disabilities into the community.

General Description:
Systems Advocacy

Multi-lingual: ASL (American Sign Language), Spanish

Membership Organization?: No

Issues: Constituencies:
Disability Rights   Disabled People
Health Care
Housing
Homelessness
Human Rights

CENTER FOR LAW & SOCIAL JUSTICE OF MEDGAR EVERS

1473 Fulton Street
Brooklyn, NY 11216

Phone: 718-953-8400
Fax: 718-467-1399
Contact: Esmeralda Simmons,
Director or Carol Dean
Archer, Sr. Project Assoc.

Office Hours: Mon. - Fri., 9am-5pm
Staff: Paid and volunteer
Geographic Scope: City-wide

Organizational Focus:
CLSJ represents groups and organizations in class action law suits, acts
as a public policy advocate, and
conducts several education projects.

General Description:
CLSJ is a civil rights and human rights,
advocacy, litigation and research
organization.

Organizational Resources:
Maintains data bank on police and
racial violence information, provides
speakers on police brutality, and
other community Issues. CLSJ also
conducts a clinical, internship program for law students and provides
free legal consultation and referrals
to the public.
Regular Public Meetings: Yes
Membership Organization?: No

Issues: Constituencies:
Legal   Multi-Racial
Social Justice   African American
Anti-Racism   Caribbean
Anti-Violence   Latino/Hispanic
Education

CENTER FOR REPRODUCTIVE LAW AND POLICY

120 Wall Street, 18th Floor
New York, NY 10005

Phone: 212-514-5534
Fax: 212-514-5538
Contact: Andrea Miller, Dir. Of
Public Education

Office Hours: 9:30am-5:30pm
Staff: Paid
Geographic Scope: National

General Description:
The Center For Reproductive Law
and Policy was founded by a
nationally recognized group of expert
reproductive rights attorneys and
activists. It is an independent
organization dedicated to ensuring
that all women have access to freely
chosen reproductive health care.
The Center's primary focus is on
those women whose reproductive
health needs have been largely
neglected: young women, low
income women, rural women, and
women of color.

Organizational Resources: Newsletter, fact sheets, workbooks for
activists, and videos.
Membership Organization?: No

Issues: Constituencies:
Reproductive Rights   Women
Legal

CENTER FOR THE ELIMINATION OF VIOLENCE

PO Box 200279
Brooklyn, NY 11220

Phone: 718-439-4612
Fax: 718-439-0016
Contact: Judith Kahan, Exec. Dir.

Office Hours: 8:00am-6pm
Staff: Paid
Geographic Scope: City-wide

Organizational Focus:
To provide a safe and healing environment for survivors of domestic violence and their children.

General Description:
CEVFI sponsors 2 programs: women's survival space, a shelter for battered women and children, a children's growing place, and a day care center for the children of residents.

Multi-lingual: Spanish, Creole, Hindi, Punjabi

Organizational Resources:
We operate a 24-hour hotline (crisis intervention, referrals) and an off-site support group for non-residents. Women interested in support group for battered women call hotline at 718-439-1000.
Membership Organization?: No

Issues: Constituencies:
Anti-Violence   Multi-Racial
Women's Rights   Women
Housing/   Youth
Homelessness

CHELSEA HOUSING GROUP, INC.

JAF Box 8361
New York, NY 10016

Phone: 212-229-1711
Fax: 212-268-9983
Contact: Bella Zuzel, Exec. Dir.

Office Hours: Mon.-Fri. 10am-6pm
Staff: Paid
Geographic Scope: Chelsea, Manhattan

Organizational Focus:
CHG is dedicated to the preservation and promotion of affordable housing to low and moderate income residents of Chelsea.

General Description:
We provide direct services in the form of individual tenant counseling, building-wide tenant organizing, advocacy and educational workshops and community forums on related housing issues.

Bi-lingual: Spanish (some staff)

Organizational Resources:
Meeting space
Regular Public Meetings: 2 times a year in the Fall & Spring
Membership Organization?: No

Issues: Constituencies:
Housing   Low Income

CHELSEA SPEAK OUT

PO Box 20170 London Terrace Sta
New York, NY 10011

Phone: 212-989-6602
Contact: Katherine Roberts

Office: No
Staff: None
Geographic Scope: Chelsea

Organizational Focus:
Advocacy for any issue which affects
Chelsea residents, whether city,
state, national or worldwide.

General Description:
We are an advocacy organization
which strives to better the lives in
our community and in the wider
community through education, action
and demonstrations, petitioning and
other communications to legislators,
etc.

Membership Organization?: Yes
Membership Requirements: Support
goals

CHILD CARE ACTION CAMPAIGN

330 7th Avenue
New York, NY 10001

Phone: 212-239-0138
Fax: 212-268-6515
Contact: Barbara Hurst, Office
Manager
Office Hours: 9am-5pm
Staff: Paid

Organizational Focus:
Respond to child care crisis nationally; help in responding to family child
care needs.

General Description:
CCAC's mission is to help provide
support for the development of programs and policies that will better
care for families and children.

Organizational Resources: Pamphlets, newsletters, and brochures.
Regular Public Meetings: 2-3 per
month
Membership Organization?: Yes
Membership Requirements: $25/
person, $50/family,
$100/organizations.

Issues:	Constituencies:
Education	Families
Human Rights	Children
Women's Rights	Women
Welfare Advocacy	
Child Care Assistance	

CHILDREN'S CREATIVE RESPONSE TO CONFLICT (CCRC)

PO Box 271, 532 N. Broadway
Nyack, NY 10960

Phone: 914-358-4601
Fax: 914-358-4924
Contact: Priscilla Prutzman, Exec. Director

Office Hours: Mon.-Fri. 9am-5pm
Staff: Paid
Geographic Scope: City-wide

Organizational Focus:
To provide specially designed activities in which adults and children experience new ways to examine conflicts and develop solutions.

General Description:
CCRC offers workshops which entail activities that allow participants to have fun while developing skills in one or more of the programs' four central themes: cooperation, communication, affirmation and conflict resolution (mediation and bias awareness).

Multi-lingual: Spanish and French

Organizational Resources:
Newsletter, pamphlets, videos and workshop facilitators.
Membership Organization?: No

Issues: Constituencies:
Anti-Racism   Youth
Multi-Racial   Lesbians/Gays
Anti-Violence   Senior
Education
Peace/Anti-Militarism
Social Justice

CHINESE STAFF AND WORKERS' ASSOCIATION

15 Catherine Street, #2R
New York, NY 10038

Phone: 212-619-7979
Fax: 212-619-8081
Contact: JoAnn Lum, Program Director

Office Hours: Sun.- Fri. 11am-7pm
Staff: Paid
Geographic Scope: City-wide

Organizational Focus:
Developing the capacity of workers to fight for their rights on the job and in the community.

General Description:
CSWA is a membership organization composed of Chinese workers of all trades, dedicated to fighting for the rights of workers in the community, including workplace rights.

Multi-lingual: Cantonese, Mandarin

Organizational Resources:
Newsletter, pamphlets, videos, ESL curriculum that addresses workers' rights and issues.
Regular Public Meetings: Yes
Membership Organization?: Yes
Membership Requirements: Chinese Worker

Issues: Constituencies:
Workers' Rights   Chinese
Immigrants' Rights   immigrants
Youth

CIRCLE OF SISTAHS

Bronx Schomburg Satellite Acad.
1010 Rev. James A. Polite Ave.
Bronx, NY 11459

Phone: 718-542-2700
Fax: 718-589-3710
Contact: Mara Benitez, Coordinator

Office Hours: Mon.-Fri. 8:30am-3pm
Staff: Volunteer
Geographic Scope: South Bronx

General Description:
Circle of Sistahs is a group of young
womyn of color in the South Bronx
working together to explore issues,
challenge sexism and racism and heal
ourselves. We analyze culture,
create our own celebrations and
rituals, and train ourselves to share
consciousness raising: each one,
teach one.

Bi-lingual: Spanish

Organizational Resources: Workshop
facilitators and a womyn's source
book (a collective journal of our
ideas, dreams, analyses, and poems.)
Regular Public Meetings: Forums and
many educational events including an
annual health fair in March and a
Womyn's Day Celebration.
Membership Organization?: Yes
Membership Requirements: Open to
all young womyn of color.

Issues:	Constituencies:
Women's Rights	Young women
Youth	of color

CITIZEN ACTION OF NEW YORK -- LEAD POISONING OUTREACH PROGRAM

271 West 125th Street, Ste. 211
New York, NY 10027

Phone: 212-961-1135
Fax: 212-961-1015
Contact: Zenaida Mendez, Project
              Director

Office Hours: 9am-5pm
Staff: Paid
Geographic Scope: City-wide

Organizational Focus:
Grassroots organizing

General Description:
We are a coalition of organizations
dedicated to creating an informed,
grassroots voice in the development
and implementation of effective
programs and policies on
environment, labor, senior citizens,
women, people of color
communities, and tenants.

Organizational Resources: Newsletter, pamphlets, videos, speakers'
bureaus, workshop facilitators, and a
meeting space.
Regular Public Meetings: Yes

Issues:	Constituencies:
Social Justice	Multi-Racial
Environment	

CITIZEN SOLDIER

175 Fifth Avenue, Suite 808
New York, NY 10010

Phone: 212-777-3470
Contact: Tod Ensign, Director

Office Hours: 10am-6pm
Geographic Scope: City-wide and national

Organizational Focus:
We are a GI/veterans' rights advocacy organization, working with current and former members of the US military.

General Description:
We provide legal representation, educational outreach, and political organization for active duty GIs and veterans who are fighting to defend their civil and human rights. We work to infuse an awareness of anti-militaristic thinking within the armed forces.

Organizational Resources: Videos, publications, our newspaper *On Guard*, brochures on various issues such as military enlistment, HIV testing in the military, and criminal justice issues.
Membership Organization?:Yes
Membership Requirement: $15 annual donation

Issues:	Constituencies:
Veteran	Veterans
Peace/Anti-Militarism	African American
Crime/	Youth
Criminal Justice	Lesbian/Gay

CITIZEN'S COMMITTEE FOR CHILDREN OF NEW YORK

105 East 22nd Street
New York, NY 10010

Phone: 212 673-1800
Fax: 212-979-5063
Contact: Gail Nayowitn, Exec. Dir.

Office Hours: Mon.-Fri. 9am-5pm
Staff: Paid and volunteer
Geographic Scope: City-wide

Organizational Focus:
CCC champions children who cannot vote, lobby, or act on their own behalf, especially those who are poor, have special needs or are particularly vulnerable. Our goal is to secure the rights, protection and services children deserve.

Organizational Resources: Newsletter, publications including *Action Guide for Helping New York City Children, Keeping Track of New York City's Children* and factsheets
Membership Organization?: Yes
Membership Requirements: Interested in same goals

Issues:	Constituencies:
Legislative	Children
Budget	Youth
Policy Analysis	
Advocacy	

CITY LIMITS COMMUNITY INFORMATION SERVICE

40 Prince Street
New York, NY 10012

Phone: 212-925-9820
Fax: 212-966-3407
Contact: Andrew White, Editor/
          Executive Director

Office?: Yes
Staff: Paid

Geographic Scope: City-wide
Organizational Focus:
City Limits is a monthly urban affairs
news magazine focusing on the
revitalization of New York's
neighborhoods.

General Description:
We offer news analysis and
investigative reporting on
government and the nonprofit
community. We cover housing,
community organizing, economic
development and other topics.

Organizational Resources: Magazine
available by subscription, forums and
workshops.
Membership Organization?: Yes
Membership Requirements: $20
yr./$35 for government & businesses.

Issues: Constituencies:
Media   Multi-Racial
Housing/Homelessness
Econ. Development
Welfare Advocacy
Environment

CITY LORE: THE NEW YORK CENTER FOR URBAN FOLK CULTURE

72 East First Street
New York, NY 10003

Phone: 212-529-1955
Fax: 212-529-5062
Contact: Steve Zeitlin, Director

Office Hours: 9:30am-5:30pm
Staff: Paid
Geographic Scope: City-wide

Organizational Focus:
City Lore is dedicated to
documenting, presenting and
advocating for the living cultural
heritage of New York City.

General Description:
City Lore advocates for New York's
"Endangered Spaces," (cherished
community establishments & land-
marks), as well as for the city's street
performers and ethnic clubs. We
sponsor a folk cultural film festival
and People's Hall of Fame Awards.

Multi-lingual: Spanish and Portuguese

Organizational Resources:
Newsletter, slide show on NYC's
traditions, arts in education
programs; photo stock house and
archives
Membership Organization?: Yes
Membership Requirements:
Contribution of $25

Issues: Constituencies:
Arts/Culture   Multi-Racial
Anti-Racism   Youth
Immigrants' Rights   Seniors
Education

CITY-WIDE TASK FORCE ON HOUSING COURT

666 Broadway, 4th Floor
New York, NY 10012

Phone: 212 982-5512
Fax: 212-982-3036
Contact: Angelita Anderson, Exec.
          Director

Office Hours: 9am-5pm
Staff: Paid
Geographic Scope: City-wide

Organizational Focus:
Housing court reform and assistance
to tenants and small property
owners.

General Description:
To address the needs of pro-se
parties (unrepresented by atty.) by
providing information which will
enable them to effectively pursue
their claims in housing court,
conducting research, making recom-
mendations and issuing reports to
improve this court.

Bi-lingual: Spanish

Regular Public Meetings: Yes
Membership Organization?: Yes

Issues: Constituencies:
Housing/   Tenants
Homelessness   Residents
Gov't Accountability

CITYWIDE WELFARE ADVOCACY NETWORK (CWAN)

2070 Grand Concourse, Suite 1
Bronx, NY 10457

Phone: 718-731-3114
Fax: 718-901-1586
Contact: Lara Broadfield,
          Coordinator

Office Hours: Mon.-Fri., 9am-5pm
Staff: Paid
Geographic Scope: City-wide

Organizational Focus:
Welfare advocacy

General Description:
CWAN organizes grassroots
individuals and organizations to
advocate for the rights of public
assistance recipients and for systemic
changes while educating ourselves
and others to be knowledgeable
about entitlement rules and
regulations. CWAN's network spans
four boroughs.

Regular Public Meetings: Network
Meetings in all 4 boroughs.
Membership Organization?: Yes
Membership Requirements: Meeting
Attendance

Issues: Constituencies:
Welfare Advocacy   Women
                     Multi-Racial

COALITION FOR A LIVABLE WEST SIDE

PO Box 78, Ansonia Station
New York, NY 10023

Phone: 212-580-9319
Contact: Madeline Polayes, Exec.
           Director

Office?:   No
Staff: Volunteer
Geographic Scope: Manhattan

Organizational Focus:
To keep the community informed
about development projects that will
impact negatively on the environment
and result in secondary displacement.

General Description:
The coalition provides information
on development proposals, zoning
issues, water, waste, transportation
and other environmental issues. We
expose the waste of government
funds to subsidize wealthy mega-
developers, raise money for legal
services in defense of quality of life
on the west side and to protect the
environment.

Organizational Resources:
Newsletter with an events calendar
and reports on local meetings.
Regular Public Meetings: Yes
Minimum once a year
Membership Organization?: Yes

Issues:
Environment
Education
Gov't Accountability

COALITION FOR KOREAN AMERICAN VOTERS, INC.

38 West 32nd Street, Suite 904
New York, NY 10001

Phone: 212-967-8428
Fax: 212-967-8652
E-mail: CKAVNY@aol.com
Contact: Charlton Rhee,
           Coordinator

Office Hours: 9am-5pm
Staff: Volunteer
Geographic Scope: City-wide

Organizational Focus:
To promote voter registration and
education of Korean Americans.

General Description:
Established in 1991, CKAV is a non-
profit, non-partisan coalition of
organizations and individuals
dedicated to promoting voter
registration and political awareness
among Korean Americans. CKAV
encourages the active and informed
participation of Korean American
voters in the political process.

Bi-lingual: Korean

Organizational Resources: News
letter, pamphlets, brochures,
membership kit.
Regular Public Meetings: 1st
Wednesday of month at 6:30pm.
Membership Organization?: Yes
Membership Requirements: Support
CKAV's purpose.

Issues: Constituencies:
Voting Rights   Asian/Pacific
Education   Islanders

COALITION FOR SOCIAL AND ECONOMIC JUSTICE

c/o Ann Eagan 39-51 46th Street
Sunnyside, NY 11104

Phone: 718-482-0170
Contact: Ann Eagan, Chair

Office?:   No
Staff: Volunteer
Geographic Scope: Queens

Organizational Focus:
Working for single national health
plan and to stop privatization of two
Queens city hospitals.

General Description:
We work in coalition with labor
unions, church groups, and other
activists. We have been focused on
Queens and Elmhurst Hospitals.
Presently doing public education and
outreach, and organizing rallies.

Organizational Resources: Speakers
on health care issues.
Regular Public Meetings: Monthly
Membership Organization?: Yes
Membership Requirements: $5
Membership Dues

Issues: Constituencies:
Econ. Development   Low & middle
Privatization   income
Social Justice   Queens'
                     community
                     residents

COALITION FOR THE HOMELESS

89 Chambers Street, 3rd Fl.
New York, NY 10007

Phone: 212-964-5900
Fax: 212-964-1303
Contact: Mary Brosnahan, Executive
           Director

Office Hours: 9am-6pm
Staff: Paid
Geographic Scope: City-wide

Organizational Focus:
CFH is the nation's oldest and most
progressive advocacy and direct
service organization fighting to end
modern, mass homelessness.

General Description:
In addition to our ground breaking
litigation and grass roots activism,
CFH runs a dozen service programs
including a mobile soup kitchen, a
sleep-away camp for homeless
children, permanent housing for
homeless families and individuals and
PWAs, job training and crisis
intervention.

Bi-lingual: Spanish

Organizational Resources:
Newsletter, pamphlets, reports, and
meeting space.
Regular Public Meetings: Yes
Monthly Client Advisory Group Mtgs.
Membership Organization?: No

Issues: Constituencies:
Housing/   Multi-Racial
Homelessness
Anti-Violence
HIV/AIDS
Health Care
Social Justice

COALITION OF ASIAN PACIFIC AMERICANS, INC. (CAPA)

c/o JASSI-275 7th Avenue, 21st Fl
New York, NY 10001

Phone: 212-255-1881
Fax: 212-255-3281
Contact: Cyril Nishimoto, Steering
          Committee Chair
Office: None. Contact through
          JASSI
Staff: Volunteer
Geographic Scope: City-wide

Organizational Focus:
CAPA's principal activity is the organizing of the annual Asian Pacific American heritage festival, usually held first Saturday of May.

General Description:
CAPA seeks to preserve the cultural heritages of Asian Pacific Americans, foster respect among them and with others, and promote the public good through programs to eliminate prejudice and encourage tolerance.

Organizational Resources: Souvenir program booklet listing the Asian Pacific American community organizations, performing groups, and supporters who participated in the annual Asian Pacific American Heritage Festival.
Membership Organization?: No

Issues: Constituencies:
Arts/Culture   Asian/Pacific
                   Islander

COALITION OF BATTERED WOMEN'S ADVOCATES

666 Broadway, Suite 520
New York, NY 10012

Phone: 212-673-7754
Fax: 212-982-3321
Contact: Toby Willner,
          Coordinator

Office Hours: Monday & Wed. 1-6pm
Staff: Paid
Geographic Scope: City-wide

Organizational Focus:
Ending violence in the lives of women.

General Description:
CBWA is multi-cultural organization of community based programs. We aim to increase public awareness of violence in intimate relationships and bring about systemic and societal change in the treatment of battered women through advocacy, education and action.

Organizational Resources: News letter, publications like *Twice Abused: Battered Women and the Criminal Justice System in NYC* and *A Guide to Orders of Protection.* We also have speakers and other resources.
Membership Organization?: No

Issues: Constituencies:
Domestic Violence   Women
Women's Rights
Anti-Violence

COALITION OF INSTITUTIONALIZED AGED AND DISABLED, INC. (CIAD)

425 East 25th Street
New York, NY 10010

Phone: 212-481-4348
Fax: 212-481-5069
Contact: Geoff Lieberman,
          Executive Director

Office Hours: 9am-5pm
Staff: Paid
Geographic Scope: City-wide

Organizational Focus:
CIAD is a coalition of nursing home and adult home resident councils dedicated to protecting and promoting the rights of residents .

General Description:
CIAD provides residents with the skills and information they need to advocate for themselves. We do this through rights education, leadership training , organizing and involving residents in public policy issues.

Organizational Resources: Video-"Resident Council a Voice for Quality of Life"
Membership Organization?: Yes, nursing home or adult home resident

Issues:	Constituencies:
Disability Rights	Disabled people
Mentally impaired	Seniors
Seniors	Mentally
Health Care	impaired people

COALITION OF LABOR UNION WOMEN, NYC CHAPTER

386 Park Ave South, 6th Floor
New York, NY 10016

Phone: 718-595-3843
Contact: Leona White, President

Office?: No
Staff: None
Geographic Scope: City-wide, but affiliated with national organization in Washington, DC.

General Description:
CLUW engages in educational and lobbying work to increase affirmative action, organize the unorganized, increase the role of women in their unions and do legislative and political action work.

Organizational Resources:
Newsletter, speakers, workshops.
Regular Public Meetings: Quarterly
Membership Organization?: Yes
Membership Requirements: Union Membership

Issues:	Constituencies:
Workers' Rights	Women
Women's Rights	Labor
Disability Rights	
Education	
Reproductive Rights	

COALITION VS. PBS CENSORSHIP

171 Madison Ave., Suite 1006
New York, NY 10016

Phone: 212-251-0817
Fax: 212-695-8970
Contact: Joanne Doroshow, East
          Coast Director

Office Hours: 10am-6pm
Staff: Volunteer
Geographic Scope: City-wide

Organizational Focus:
Exposing the impact of corporate
dependency and lack of public
accountability at PBS.

General Description:
A broad membership organization
involving filmmakers, activists,
celebrities, and average Americans
concerned about and fighting public
TV censorship.

Organizational Resources:
Informational packets, speakers.
Membership Organization?: No

Issues:
Media

COLOMBIA MULTIMEDIA PROJECT

PO Box 1091
New York, NY 10116-1091

Phone: 212-802-7209
Fax: 718-369-4182
Contact: Mario Munillo, Victoria
          Maldonado, Coordinators

Office: None
Staff: Volunteer
Geographic Scope: City-wide

Organizational Focus:
CMP is a grassroots community
organization aimed at educating the
US public about Colombia and the
Colombian community in the US.

General Description:
Through the use of video and audio
productions and public forums, CMP
tries to shed a more comprehensive
light on the present realities facing
Colombia and the Colombian
community in New York. We work
in conjunction with the Colombia
Human Rights Network.

Bi-lingual: Spanish

Organizational Resources: Videos and
audio tapes; a quarterly news bulletin;
public forums.
Regular Public Meetings: Yes, call for
details
Membership Organization?: No

Issues:	Constituencies:
Human Rights	Latino/Hispanic
Int'l Solidarity	Multi-Racial
Social Justice	
Media	
Immigrants' Rights	
Drug War	

COLORLIFE! MAGAZINE

301 Cathedral Parkway, Box 287
New York, NY 10026

Phone: 212-222-9794
Contact: Lidell Jackson

Office Hours: None
Staff: Volunteer
Geographic Scope: City-wide

General Description:
COLORLife! is a quarterly magazine
covering issues affecting the Lesbian,
Gay, two spirit and bisexual People
of color community. Founded in
June 1991, COLORLife! has provided
local, national, and international news
and feature coverage of the
community.

Organizational Resources: Each issue
carries a special section "Speaking for
Ourselves" a resource directory of
organizations for the Lesbian, Gay,
Two spirit and bisexual People of
Color Community.
Membership Organization?: No

Issues: Constituencies:
Lesbian/Gay   Multi-racial
Anti-Racism   Lesbian/Gay
International Solidarity

COMMISSION ON THE PUBLIC'S HEALTH SYSTEM (CPHS)

c/o Patients' Rights Hotline
215 West 125th Street, Rm. 400
New York, NY 10027

Phone: 212-316-9393
Contact: Nilka Alvarez, Education/
          Outreach Coordinator

Office Hours: Mon.-Fri. 9am-5pm
Staff: Paid
Geographic Scope: City-wide

Organizational Focus:
Support the public sector in health
care to provide equal access and
quality care for all New Yorkers.

General Description:
A coalition of health advocates,
community groups, health care
workers, patients who support
alternatives to privatization of public
services, share a commitment to
community education and organization for accessible, universal, quality
and publicly accountable health care.

Bi-lingual: Spanish

Organizational Resources:
Educational materials, speakers'
bureau, training workshops on health
care issues.
Regular Public Meetings: Monthly.
Times vary, call for details.
Membership Requirements:
Commitment to work on goals,
agreement with principles

Issues: Constituencies:
Health Care   Multi-Racial
                            Poor/working
                            class
                            Uninsured

COMMITTEE AGAINST ANTI-ASIAN VIOLENCE

191 East 3rd Street
New York, NY 10009

Phone: 212-473-6485
Fax: 212-473-5569
Contact: Anannya Bhattacharjee
          Exec. Director

Office Hours: 10am-6pm
Staff: Paid
Geographic Scope: City-wide

Organizational Focus:
Organize Asian communities to
combat racism, police violence, and
economic injustice.

General Description:
We seek to empower Asian American communities through community
organizing, public education, leadership development, direct action, and
media activism to address violence
and the conditions that render Asians
vulnerable to violence.

Multi-lingual: Korean, Cantonese,
Vietnamese, Urdu, Hindi and Bengali

Organizational Resources: Newsletter, pamphlets, clippings file,
speakers, workshop facilitators and
videos.
Membership Organization?: Yes
Membership Requirements:
Committee participation

Issues: Constituencies:
Anti-Racism   Asian/Pacific
Anti-Violence   Islander
Social Justice   Multi-Racial
Criminal Justice
Economic Injustice
Workers' Rights

COMMITTEE FOR A NUCLEAR-FREE ISLAND, INC.

PO Box 509
Staten Island, NY 10314

Phone: 718-979-6563
Fax: 718-667-4740
Contact: Ronald Bel, President

Office?: No
Staff: None
Geographic Scope: Staten Island and
Brooklyn

Organizational Focus:
Nuclear and radioactive concerns

General Description:
The committee opposes nuclear
weapons, power plants, and waste
dumping.

Organizational Resources: Leaflets,
speakers, and our newsletter
Nukenotes.
Regular Public Meetings: Monthly
Membership Organization?: No

Issues:
Peace/Anti-Militarism
Social Justice
Environment
Econ. Development
Human Rights

COMMITTEE FOR BETTER TRANSIT, INC.

Box 3106
Long Island, NY 11103

Phone: 718-728-0091
Contact: Stephen Dobrow, Pres.

Office?:   No
Staff: Volunteer
Geographic Scope: City-wide

Organizational Focus:
Transit and planning issues

General Description:
To promote improved multi-modal regional transportation by bringing together users and experts to work on solutions.

Organizational Resources:
Newsletters, reports, pamphlets, speakers, technical assistance.
Membership Organization?:   Yes
Membership Requirements:
Dues/Interest

Issues:
Transportation
Econ. Development
Environment

COMMITTEE FOR HUMANITARIAN ASSISTANCE TO IRANIAN REFUGEES, INC.

PO Box 7051, GPO
New York, NY 10116

Phone: 212-714-8095
Fax: Same/Call first
Contact: Maryann Namazie, Exec.
           Director

Office?:   No.
Staff: Paid
Geographic Scope: City-wide

Organizational Focus:
Assisting Iranian refugees and asylum seekers irrespective of race, religion, gender, political opinion or sexual orientation.

General Description:
CHAIR's mission is to advocate and facilitate empowerment through rights education. We provide access to tools, resources and support to promote and protect their rights.

Bi-lingual: Persian (Farsi)

Organizational Resources: Newsletter, information, support materials.
Membership Organization?: No

Issues:	Constituencies:
Immigrants' Rights	Iranian
Women's Rights	
Human Rights	

COMMITTEE FOR INTERNATIONAL HUMAN RIGHTS INQUIRY

c/o Ruth H. Wilson
415 Grand Street, #E-1905
New York, NY 10002

Phone: 212-674-3762
Contact: Ruth Wilson, Secy.

Office?:   No
Staff: None
Geographic Scope: City-wide base & national

Organizational Focus:
Human rights

General Description:
Assistance to all social service workers, clients, human rights monitors, groups and nations involving social service workers that are being persecuted. Assistance to other organizations involved in human rights problems. Opposition to the death penalty, abusive prison conditions, economic deprivation and other forms of discrimination and injury. Cooperation with social service organizations here and abroad. ·

Organizational Resources: Information on social service workers whose human rights are violated. Speeches and interviews from contacts in various countries, and speakers are available.
Regular Public Meetings: Yes
Membership Organization?: Yes
Membership Requirements: Dues

Issues:	Constituencies:
Human Rights	Social Service
Social Justice	Workers
Int'l Solidarity	

COMMUNITY FOOD RESOURCE CENTER, INC.

90 Washington Street
New York, NY 10006

Phone: 212-344-0195
Fax: 212-344-1422
Contact: Kathy Goldman, Exec. Dir.

Office Hours: 8:30am-6 pm
Staff: Paid
Geographic Scope: City-wide

Organizational Focus:
Community Food Resource Center focuses on food, hunger, nutrition and income issues in New York City.

General Description:
Our primary goal is to increase access to nutritious food at reasonable cost for all New Yorkers, especially the hundreds of thousands of families and individuals living in poverty. CFRC is both an advocacy and direct service organization.

Multi-lingual: Spanish and Creole

Organizational Resources: CFRC has informational materials on food programs, entitlements and benefits, welfare issues, etc. Most are available in English, Spanish, Creole and some in Chinese and Russian.
Regular Public Meetings: Monthly

Issues:
Anti-Hunger
Welfare Advocacy
Housing/Homelessness
Econ. Development
Senior

COMMUNITY HEALTH PROJECT, INC.

208 West 13th Street, 2nd Fl.
New York, NY 10011

Phone: 212-675-3559
Fax: 212-645-0013
Contact: Robert Mauer, Clinic
            Manager

Office Hours: M-Th 10-9 & Fri 10-6
               1st and 3rd Saturdays
Staff: Paid and volunteer
Geographic Scope: City-wide

Organizational Focus:
Health Care

General Description:
NY's only lesbian and gay health
facility providing medical services,
health education, peer counseling for
adults and adolescents regardless of
ability to pay.

Bi-lingual: Spanish

Organizational Resources: Low cost ,
high quality health care for sexual
minority people.
Membership Organization?: Yes

Issues:	Constituencies:
Health Care	Lesbian/Gay
Lesbian/Gay	Transgender
HIV/AIDS	Youth

COMMUNITY WORKS

30 West 70th Street
New York, NY 10023

Phone: 212-724-3037
Fax: 212-724-2458
Contact: Barbara Horowitz, Dir.

Office Hours: 8am-5pm
Staff: Paid
Geographic Scope: City-wide

Organizational Focus:
Community Works believes in using
the arts to connect underserved
youth in New York and California
with community organizations and
artists.

General Description:
We are dedicated to supporting
disadvantaged youth and
neighborhood cultural institutions,
promoting community pride and
discussions, and providing local
advocacy role models for students to
inspire positive social change.

Organizational Resources: We
publish a calendar of events that is
distributed to teachers throughout
the public school system.
Membership Organization?: No

Issues:	Constituencies:
Youth	Youth
Arts/Culture	Multi-Racial
Education	

CONSUMER ACTION PROGRAM OF BEDFORD STUYVESANT/CABS

7 Debevoise Street
Brooklyn, NY 11206

Phone: 718-388-1601
Contact: William Pernisek, Director

Office Hours: 9am-5pm
Staff: Paid
Geographic Scope: Central Brooklyn

Organizational Focus:
Community economic development

General Description:
Undertakes development of community-owned economic development enterprises designed to control services, employ residents, provide community cash flow and create community infrastructure. Currently employs 2000 residents in 5 separate businesses involved in home care, nursing care and housing.

Bi-lingual: Spanish

Membership Organization?: No

Issues:	Constituencies:
Econ. Development	Multi-Racial
Health Care	Latino/Hispanic
Housing/	Seniors
Homelessness	

COOPER SQUARE COMMITTEE

61 East 4th Street
New York, NY 10003

Phone: 212-228-8210
Fax: 212-477-5328
Contact: Val Orselli, Director

Office Hours: 9am-5pm, Mon.-Fri.
Staff: Paid
Geographic Scope: Lower East Side

General Description:
Planning and organizing for the development and preservation of affordable housing. We are the oldest anti-displacement organization in the United States.

Multi-lingual: Spanish, Italian, Ukranian

Organizational Resources: Pamphlets, video, information on tenants' rights, social services
Regular Public Meetings: At least three times a year
Membership Organization?: Yes
Membership Requirements: Must live or work in the Cooper Square urban renewal area, which is East 14th Street to Delancey, Bowery/Third Avenue to First Avenue.

Issues:	Constituencies:
Housing/	Multi-Racial
Homelessness	Working class
Econ. Development	Low & moderate income people

COORDINADORA DE LA CULTURA POPULAR

c/o 63 South Portland Avenue
Brooklyn, NY 11217

Contact: Soraya Marcano, Director

Office: None
Staff: None

Organizational Focus:
Latino artists

General Description:
We organize Latino artists, trying to bring their work to more people. We hope to increase solidarity and exchanges between artists and their communities.

Bi-lingual: Spanish

Regular Public Meetings: No
Membership Organization?: No

Issues: Constituencies:
Arts/Culture   Latino/Hispanic

CROWN HEIGHTS YOUTH COLLECTIVE

915 Franklin Avenue
Brooklyn, NY 11225

Phone: 718-756-7600
Fax: 718-773-7052
Contact: Bob Carter

Office Hours: 8am-8:30pm
Staff: Paid and volunteer
Geographic Scope: Central Brooklyn, Crown Heights

Organizational Focus:
Provide a comprehensive youth program using a hands-on approach to encourage young people to re-focus.

General Description:
CHYC is a self development program located in Central Brooklyn since 1978. We provide for youth employment and education counseling, summer academy, cultural services. Although we continue to target youth 7-21, our services are available to the community at large.

Membership Organization?: No

Issues: Constituencies:
Self-Development   Youth
Anti-Racism   Multi-Racial
Anti-Violence
Arts/Culture

CUBA INFORMATION PROJECT

198 Broadway, Suite 800
New York, NY 10038

Phone: 212-227-3422
Fax: 212-227-4859
Contact: Leslie Cagan, Director

Office Hours: Mon.-Fri., 9am-5pm
Staff: Paid and volunteer
Geographic Scope: National

Organizational Focus:
Resource and information center for groups working to end the US economic blockade of Cuba.

General Description:
We provide educational materials, organizing resources, Congressional lobbying updates and news from Cuba. Our publication, Cuba Action, and other materials offer a link to the growing movement to normalize relations with Cuba.

Organizational Resources:
Newsletter, pamphlets, fact sheets, speakers, Congressional updates, news from Cuba, speakers, videos and books.
Regular Public Meetings: Yes
Membership Organization?: No

Issues:
Int'l Solidarity
Peace/Anti-Militarism

DEEP DISH TELEVISION NETWORK

339 Lafayette Street, 3rd Floor
New York, NY 10012

Phone: 212-473-8933
Fax: 212-420-8223
Contact: Cynthia López, Acting
               Executive Director

Office Hours: T,W, Th. 10am-6pm
Staff: Paid
Geographic Scope: City-wide

Organizational Focus:
A national satellite network of producers, activists, media advocates, and grassroots organizations. We distribute programming via satellite to public, municipal, educational access channels and to PBS systems.

General Description:
We co-produce and distribute programming featuring activists that work on environmental issues, housing and homelessness, criminal justice, social justice, racism, civil liberties and AIDS. These programs are produced by young people, women, gays and lesbians, working people, youth and seniors.

Bi-lingual: Spanish

Organizational Resources: Videos
Regular Public Meetings: No
Membership Organization?: No

Issues:	Constituencies:
Media	Multi-Racial
Social Justice	Multi-Cultural
Arts/Culture	Multi-Class

DISABILITY INDEPENDENCE DAY MARCH

Contact: Naomi Bodo, Chairperson or Ellen Nuzzi

Phone: Bodo day 212-442-3983
Bodo eve. 212-977-6063
Nuzzi day 718-488-1215
Staff: Volunteer
Geographic Scope: City-wide

Organizational Focus:
To annually celebrate the signing of the Americans with Disabilities Act (ADA) to highlight issues concerning the rights of people with disabilities to equality in our city.

General Description:
To educate people with disabilities, their families, friends and the community generally about the need for attitudinal, architectural, and communication access to bring dignity, empowerment and equality to all.

Bi-lingual: Sign language for the deaf

Organizational Resources: Newsletter, videos, speakers, workshops regarding the ADA, attitudinal training and advocacy training.
Regular Public Meetings: First week of each month. Call for details.
Membership Organization?: No

Issues:
Disability Rights
Gov't Accountability
Voting Rights
Health Care
Human Rights
Social Justice

Constituencies:
Persons with disabilities
Multi-Racial
Women

DISABLED IN ACTION OF METROPOLITAN NEW YORK

PO Box 30954, Port Authority
New York, NY 10011

Phone: 718-261-3737
Contact: Frieda Zames, VP
Office?: No

Staff: None
Geographic Scope: City-wide

Organizational Focus:
Disabled people's rights.

General Description:
Disabled In Action (DIA) is a civil rights group dedicated to improving the legal, social and economic condition of people with disabilities so that they may achieve complete integration into society.

Organizational Resources:
Newsletter, brochure, monthly radio program on WBAI.
Regular Public Meetings: Last Sunday of month, Sept.-May.
Membership Organization?: Yes
Membership Requirements: Annual Dues $3-$25

Issues:
Disability Rights
Health Care
Human Rights
Social Justice
Housing/Homelessness

Constituencies:
Disabled People
Multi-Racial
Lesbian/Gay

DOMINICAN WOMEN'S CAUCUS

PO Box 5602 Manhattanville Sta.
New York, NY 10027

Phone: 718-882-2921
Contact: Genara Necos, President

Office?: No
Staff: Volunteer
Geographic Scope: City-wide

Organizational Focus:
Founded in 1991 to unite Dominican women to identify and find solutions to the problems that affect them.

General Description:
The Caucus promotes social, political educational and cultural activities that lead to the development of women. We establish ties with similar organizations; fight against negative practices and attitudes affecting women; and support the struggle of Latin American women in general.

Bi-lingual: Spanish

Organizational Resources:
Speakers on Latino community, political empowerment and other women's issues, workshop on breast cancer, annual youth outreach program and seminars.
Regular Public Meetings: 1st Saturday of month
Membership Organization?: Yes
Membership Requirements: Monthly Dues

Issues:	Constituencies:
Women's Rights	Latino/Hispanic
Anti-Violence	Women
Immigrants' Rights	Multi-Racial
Education	
Econ. Development	

DOMINICAN WOMEN'S DEVELOPMENT CENTER, INC.

359 Fort Washington Ave. Ste 1G
New York, NY 10033

Phone: 212-740-1929
Fax: 212-740-8352
Contact: Ana Ventura, Secretary

Office Hours: 9:00 am-5:00pm
Staff: Paid
Geographic Scope: Washington Heights/Inwood

Organizational Focus:
To unite Dominican and other Latina women to seek solutions to the problems affecting them in their daily lives.

General Description:
We have an educational development program that includes English as a Second Language and Spanish Literacy classes; a personal development program that includes information and referrals, peer counseling, immigration services and educational workshops; and an economic development program that includes training in clerical skills, job placement and development of small enterprises.

Bi-lingual: Spanish

Membership Organization?: Yes
Membership Requirements:
Attendance at three meetings, being Latina and paying dues.

Issues:	Constituencies:
Education	Latino/Hispanic
Econ. Development	Women
Women's Rights	
Immigrants' Rights	

THE DOOR -- A CENTER OF ALTERNATIVES

121 Avenue of Americas
New York, NY 10013

Phone: 212-941-9090
Fax: 212-941-0714
Contact: Kathleen Connoly,
          Development Dir.

Office Hours: Administration: M-F 8am-6pm, Program: M,W,Th, F 3:00-9:30pm & Tues. 3:30- 9:30
Staff: Paid and volunteer
Geographic Scope: City-wide

Organizational Focus:
The Door provides comprehensive, integrated services to disadvantaged youth ages 12-21. Our goal is to assist you in a holistic manner that supports your healthy growth and development.

General Description:
The Door helps young people side-step the red tape of the human services system. Its founders combined expertise of professionals from a variety of disciplines to create a center that today offers more than 20 different programs and services on site -- all designed to meet the developmental needs of adolescents.

Multi-lingual: Spanish, Russian, Polish and Chinese

Organizational Resources:
Newsletter, pamphlets, tours, training, education programs, technical assistance.
Membership Organization?: No

Issues: Constituencies:
Youth   Youth
Arts/Culture

DOWNTOWN COMMUNITY TELEVISION CENTER

87 Lafayette Street
New York, NY 10013

Phone: 212-966-4510
Fax: 212-219-0248
Contact: Hye Jung Park

Office Hours: Mon.-Fri. 10am-6pm
Staff: Paid and volunteer
Geographic Scope: City-wide

Organizational Focus:
Non-profit media arts center serving arts, activist, and minority communities.

General Description:
Provide basic and advanced video production trainings, screenings, youth programs, and access to equipment at low cost or free.

Multi-lingual: Spanish, Chinese

Organizational Resources:
Newsletter, video, meeting space, video consultation
Membership Organization?: Yes
Membership Requirements: $30/Year

Issues: Constituencies:
Arts/Culture   Multi-Racial
Education   Women
Media   Youth
                   Lesbian/Gay

EAST SIDE PEACE ACTION

114 E. 32nd Street, Rm. 906
New York, NY 10016

Phone: 212-683-7906
Fax: 212-447-6628
Contact: Alex Smith, Chair

Office Hours: 1:00pm-5:30pm
Staff: Robert Bogen,
             Coordinator
Geographic Scope: East Side of
Manhattan

Organizational Focus:
Peace education and disarmament.

General Description:
One chapter of the Metropolitan
Peace Action Committee dedicated
in the struggle to achieve peace.

Regular Public Meetings: Bi-monthly
Membership Organization?: Yes
Membership Requirements: Dues,
$25; limited income $15.

Issues:	Constituencies:
Peace/	Multi-Racial
Anti-Militarism	Women
Media	Latino/Hispanic
Anti-Racism	Youth
Anti-Violence	

ECONOMISTS ALLIED FOR ARMS REDUCTION (ECAAR)

25 West 45 Street Suite 1401
New York, NY 10036

Phone: 212-768-2080
Fax: 212-768-2167
Contact: Alice Slater, Exec. Dir.

Office Hours: Mon.-Fri. 9:30-5:30pm
Staff: Paid
Geographic Scope: City-wide

Organizational Focus:
To shift global spending away from
the military and towards human and
environmental needs.

General Description:
ECAAR uses the expertise of economists to find ways to reduce global
military spending, provide research
that empowers grassroots activists,
end the arms trade, stop nuclear
proliferation, encourage greater
reliance on the United Nations, and
influence public policy in favor of
deeper military spending cuts.

Organizational Resources:
Newsletter -- *ECAAR News
Network, Peace Science, and Public
Policy Journal*, videos & transcripts of
speaking events, fact sheets &
research papers presented at
conferences.
Membership Organization?: Yes
Membership Requirements: $35 basic
membership, $10 for students

Issues:	Constituencies:
Peace Conversion	Multi-Racial
Anti-Militarism	
Environment	

ECUELECUA INTERARTS PERFORMANCE COLLECTIVE

PO Box 2171
New York, NY 10009

Phone: 212-674-5311
Fax: 212-477-2579
Contact: Maria Mar, Exec. Director

Office Hours: Mon.-Wed. 12-6pm
Staff: Paid and volunteer
Geographic Scope: City-wide

Organizational Focus:
Life skills and self-empowerment
through the arts, focusing on women,
people of color and youth. We have
special interest in gender issues,
including gender violence and sexism.

General Description:
Ecuelecua is a multi-cultural Latino
organization combining the arts,
education and social service to
empower individuals. We offer plays,
performances and support
workshops to enhance the work of
community organizations.

Bi-lingual: Spanish

Organizational Resources:
Educational newsletter,
advocacy/education plays, support
workshops, and leadership
development workshops
Membership Organization?: No

Issues:	Constituencies:
Arts/Culture	Latino/Hispanic
Women's Rights	Women
Gender Violence	Multi-Racial
Health Care	Youth
Education	

EDUCATION CENTER FOR COMMUNITY ORGANIZING (ECCO)

c/o Hunter College
School of Social Work
129 East 79th Street
New York, NY 10021

Phone: 212 452-7112
Fax: 212-452-7150
Contact: Terry Mizrahi, Director

Office Hours: 9am-5pm
Staff: Paid and volunteer
Geographic Scope: City-wide

General Description: ECCO believes
in a world based on peace, equality,
social and economic justice and
provides forums for groups that
work toward these goals. We
promote the concept and use of
community organizing strategies; and
create forums for self-awareness,
strategy building and the exchange of
information, resources and
experiences, in particular women's
groups.

Organizational Resources: A
collection of references and
resources on women organizers.
Regular Public Meetings: Periodic
"coffee houses" and conferences
Membership Organization?:Yes
Membership Requirements: Dues
$10/individuals; $20/organizations.

Issues:
Community Organizing
Resource Development
Women's Rights
Social Justice

EDUCATIONAL VIDEO CENTER

60 East 13th Street, 4th Fl.
New York, NY 10003

Phone: 212-254-2848
Fax: 212-777-7940
Contact: Steven Goodman, Exec.
         Director

Office Hours: 9:00am-5:30pm
Staff: Paid
Geographic Scope: City-wide

General Description:
EVC provides training and support
services in documentary production
and media literacy to high school
students, teachers and community
activists. Through the process of
creating documentaries on youth and
community issues, students learn
valuable research, reporting, editing
and critical media-viewing skills. The
results are powerful educational
materials for all.

Organizational Resources: Newsletter, video documentaries available
for sale, rent, or public screenings.
Regular Public Meetings: January &
June, end of every high school
semester
Membership Organization?: No

Issues: Constituencies:
Media   Youth
Students   Multi-Racial
Education   Inner City
Youth   Families
Empowerment

EDUCATORS FOR SOCIAL RESPONSIBILITY

475 Riverside Drive, Room 450
New York, NY 10115

Phone: 212-870-3318
Fax: 212-870-2464
Contact: Michael Hirschhorn,
         Deputy Director

Office Hours: 9am-5pm
Staff: Paid
Geographic Scope: City-wide

Organizational Focus:
To make social responsibility an
integral part of education by fostering new ways of teaching and learning.

General Description:
E.S.R. coordinates conflict resolution,
diversity and violence prevention
programs in 150 schools and community organizations. Projects include
the Multicultural Education Project,
Schools Teaching Options For Peace,
and the Community-Based Organization Training Project.

Multi-lingual: Spanish, Chinese and
Haitian Creole

Organizational Resources:
Newsletters, workshop facilitators,
pamphlets, videos, creative
supplementary teaching manuals.
Regular Public Meetings: Monthly
forums of Multicultural Educ. Project.
Membership Organization?: Yes
Membership Requirements? $35

Issues: Constituencies:
Education   Multi-Racial
Anti-Racism   Teachers
Anti-Violence   Administrators
Youth   Parents
Peace   Youth

EL PUENTE

211 South Fourth Street
Brooklyn, NY 11211

Phone: 718-387-0404
Fax: 718-387-6816
Contact: Yvonne Kingon

Office Hours: 7:30am-9:00pm
Staff: Paid and Volunteer
Geographic Scope: Williamsburg and Bushwick

Organizational Focus:
A community/youth development organization nurturing holistic leadership for peace and justice.

General Description:
Founding center in Williamsburg integrates family clinic, high school, visual and performing arts center, youth employment and sports/recreation program.

ELDERS SHARE THE ARTS

57 Willoughby Street
Brooklyn, NY 11201

Phone: 718-488-8565
Fax: 718-488-8296
Contact: Susan Perlstein, Director

Office Hours: Mon.-Fri. 9am-5pm
Staff: Paid and volunteer
Geographic Scope: City-wide

Organizational Focus:
Linking cultures and generations through "Living History Arts."

General Description:
Our staff of professional artists works with old and young to transform their life stories into dramatic, literary, and visual presentations which celebrate community life. We share the lifetime skills of older artists with communities who have little access to art.

Multi-lingual: Spanish, Chinese

Organizational Resources:
Our newsletter, *Cultural Connections,* pamphlets and training manuals, videos and audio cassettes of elder storytellers, meeting space, speakers, and workshops.
Regular Public Meetings: Yes
Membership Organization?: Yes
Membership Requirements: $25

Issues:	Constituencies:
Arts/Culture	Seniors
Anti-Racism	Youth

EMPIRE STATE PRIDE AGENDA (ESPA)

611 Broadway, Room 907a
New York, NY 10012

Phone: 212-673-5417
Fax: 212-673-6128
Contact: Dick Dadey, Exec. Dir.

Office Hours: 9:30am-6pm
Staff: Paid
Geographic Scope: Statewide

Organizational Focus:
Lesbian and Gay political issues.

General Description:
NY State's Lesbian and Gay political organization working for fair and equal treatment of lesbians and gay men under the law.

Organizational Resources:
Newsletter
Regular Public Meetings: Yes
Membership Organization?: Yes

Issues: Constituencies:
Lesbian/Gay   Lesbian/Gay

ENVIRONMENTAL ACTION COALITION

625 Broadway, 2nd Floor
New York, NY 10012

Phone: 212-677-1601
Fax: 212-505-8613
Contact: Steve Richardson, Exec. Director

Office Hours: Mon.-Fri. 9:30-6pm
Staff: Paid
Geographic Scope: City-wide

Organizational Focus:
Finding workable, practical solutions to urban environmental problems and getting them adopted.

General Description:
EAC works in cooperation with community-based organizations and schools in all five boroughs, working to make sure that environmental resources are available to all.

Bi-lingual: Spanish

Organizational Resources:
Newsletter, videos, pamphlets, and fact sheets on a variety of environmental topics
Membership Organization?: Yes
Membership Requirements: $20 Annual Dues

Issues: Constituencies:
Environment   Multi-Racial
Gov't Accountability Youth
Education   Women

ENVIRONMENTAL DEFENSE FUND

257 Park Avenue South
New York, NY 10010

Phone: 212-505-2100
Fax: 212-505-2375
Contact: Barbara Olshansky,
            Attorney

Office Hours: 9am - 6pm
Staff: Paid and volunteer
Geographic Scope: City-wide

Organizational Focus:
Environmental issues: pollution,
public health, regulatory reform,
citizen participation, wildlife
conservation, natural resource
conservation.

General Description:
The Environmental Defense Fund is a
national non-profit environmental
research, education and advocacy
organization comprised of attorneys,
scientists and economists.

Bi-lingual: Spanish

Organizational Resources:
Pamphlets, studies, videos, meeting
space, speakers, workshop
facilitators, technical science
newsletter, experts, hotline on lead
poisoning.
Membership Organization?: Yes
Membership Requirements: $15
Annual Membership

Issues:
Environment
Gov't Accountability
Human Rights

EVAC NEIGHBORHOOD CRIME PREVENTION

PO Box 1231- Cooper Station
New York, NY 10276

Phone: 212-459-4912
Contact: Charles Dworkis, Director

Office: No
Staff: Volunteer
Geographic Scope: Manhattan below
59th Street

Organizational Focus: Helping to
form block and tenant groups; civilian
anti-crime/anti-drug patrols; neighborhood improvement strategies.

Multi-lingual: French and Spanish

Organizational Resources: Training
manuals, newsletter and seminars.
Regular Public Meetings: First
Thursday of month
Membership Organization?: Yes
Membership Requirements: Dues
from $5-$100

Issues:
Crime/Criminal Justice

FACES

920 48th Street
Brooklyn, NY 11219

Phone: 718-283-7861
Fax: 718-283-8272
Contact: Susan Montez, CSW, Dir.

Office Hours: 9am-5pm
Staff: Paid
Geographic Scope: City-wide

General Description:
Faces is an improvisational theater
company for teens that dramatizes
issues and problems that teenagers
are facing every day.

Organizational Resources:
Workshops
Membership Organization?: Yes
Membership Requirements: Interest
in acting

Issues:	Constituencies:
Youth	Youth
Anti-Violence	Multi-Racial
Education	
HIV/AIDS	
Anti-Racism	

FAIR TRADE CAMPAIGN

410 West 25th Street
New York, NY 10001

Phone: 212-627-2314
Fax: 212-627-0637
Contact: Nikos Valance, Director

Office Hours: Mon.-Fri. 9am-5pm
Staff: Paid
Geographic Scope: City-wide

Organizational Focus:
Trade issues.

General Description:
Education and organizing regarding
trade issues.

Multi-lingual: Spanish, French,
German

Organizational Resources:
Literature on trade and workshop
facilitators.
Membership Organization?: No

Issues:
Trade Agreements
Workers' Rights
Environment
Econ. Development
Social Justice

FAIRNESS AND ACCURACY IN REPORTING (FAIR)

130 West 25th Street, 7th Fl.
New York, NY 10001

Phone: 212-633-6700
Fax: 212-727 7668
E-Mail: info@igc.apc
Contact: Sam Husseini, Activist
          Coordinator

Office Hours: Mon.-Fri. 10am-6pm
Staff: Paid and volunteer
Geographic Scope: City-wide and national

Organizational Focus:
Democratizing the major media by offering well documented criticism to correct bias.

General Description:
Focus public awareness on the narrow corporate ownership of the press, its allegiance to official agendas and insensitivity to public interest constituencies (FAIR seeks to investigate the first amendment).

Organizational Resources: Newsletter, magazine, national radio show, local media show, on-line mailing list.
Membership Organization?: Yes
Membership Requirements: $30 to subscribe to magazine. For more information, call 800-847-3993.

Issues:
Media

FEDERAL LAND ACTION GROUP (FLAG)

c/o Worldview
29 King Street, #31
New York, NY 10014

Phone: 212-924-7929
Fax: Same
Contact: John Friede, Director

Office Hours: 11am-7pm
Staff: None
Geographic Scope: City-wide

Organizational Focus:
Educate citizens of the greater New York area about threats to North American public lands.

General Description:
FLAG holds monthly meetings that address a wide range of issues including forest protection, mining, and grazing reform.

Regular Public Meetings: Monthly meeting at the Wetlands Preserve at 161 Hudson Street, NY, NY 10013 on the Third Tuesday of each month.
Membership Organization?: No

Issues: Constituencies:
Environment   Multi-Racial
Corporate Accountability
Gov't Accountability
Social Justice

FEDERATION OF PROTESTANT WELFARE AGENCIES, INC.

281 Park Avenue South
New York, NY 10010

Phone: 212-777-4800
Fax: 212-673-4085
Contact: Dr. Megan E. McLaughlin,
           Executive Director

Office Hours: 8:30am-5:30pm
Staff: Paid and volunteer
Geographic Scope: City-wide

Organizational Focus:
Poverty/income security, hunger,
welfare reform, children, youth,
families, elderly, human service infrastructure, AIDS/HIV.

General Description:
Umbrella organization providing
technical assistance, education,
training, advocacy, grants, policy
analysis and research to more than
260 non-profit agencies.

Multi-lingual: Spanish, French

Organizational Resources:
Laura Parsons Pratt Conference
Center (meeting space); group
purchasing service, training institute,
a human resource and support
center, and many publications.
Regular Public Meetings: Yes
Membership Organization?: Yes
Membership Requirements:
501(C)(3) Tax Exempt

Issues: Constituencies:
Social Justice   Families
Gov't Accountability   Protestant and
Welfare Advocacy   Non-Sectarian
Women's Rights   Orgs.
HIV/AIDS

FIFTH AVENUE COMMITTEE

199 Fourteenth Street
Brooklyn, NY 11215

Phone: 718-965-2777
Fax: 718-832-6676
Contact: Brad Lander, Exec. Dir.

Office Hours: Mon.-Fri. 9am-5pm
Staff: Paid
Geographic Scope: South B'klyn

Organizational Focus:
Affordable housing, tenants' and
welfare rights, cooperative and
mutual ownership of housing, community economic development, and
neighborhood community organizing.

General Description:
FAC aims to preserve & strengthen
the economic & racial diversity of
lower Park Slope & South Brooklyn
to ensure that all residents benefit
from the area's development.

Bi-lingual: Spanish

Organizational Resources: Newsletter, workshops on affordable
housing, tenants' rights, public
assistance, empowerment.
Regular Public Meetings: Announced
in newsletter
Membership Organization?: No

Issues: Constituencies:
Econ. Development   Multi-Racial
Housing/Homelessness
Latino/Hispanic
African American
Welfare Advocacy
Anti-Racism

FOOD & HUNGER HOTLINE

115 East 23rd Street, 10th Floor
New York, NY 10010

Phone: 212-533-7600
Fax: 212-674-1946
Contact: Stephen Pimpare

Office Hours: Mon.-Fri. 9am-5pm
Emergency Referral Hrs.: M-F 9-9
and weekends 9am-5pm
Staff: Paid and volunteer
Geographic Scope: City-wide

Organizational Focus:
Poverty, hunger, homelessness.

General Description:
Food & Hunger Hotline is New
York's oldest citywide anti-hunger
organization. Programs include:
emergency food referrals;
entitlement counseling; technical
assistance to CBO's; life skills,
parenting and nutrition workshops;
nonprofit restaurant job training;
speakers' bureau; and policy,
research and advocacy.

Bi-lingual: Spanish

Organizational Resources:
Newsletter, emergency food referral,
technical assistance, and workshops.
Membership Organization?: No

Issues:
Economic Justice
Housing/Homelessness
Social Justice

FORT GREENE COMMUNITY ACTION NETWORK

14 Metro Tech Center
Brooklyn, New York 11201

Phone: 718-694-6961
Fax: 718-852-1285
Contact: Eric Blackwell, Exec. Dir.

Office Hours: Mon.-Fri. 9am-6pm
Staff: Volunteer
Geographic Scope: Fort Greene,
Brooklyn

Organizational Focus:
Community improvement, local
development, local newspaper
publishing, networking practical
solutions.

General Description:
Identifying gaps in service delivery to
the greater Fort Greene/Clinton Hills
community.

Bi-lingual: Spanish

Organizational Resources: We are
currently developing a news hotline
to go along with our local
newspapers.
Membership Organization?:No

Issues:	Constituencies:
Media	African American
Econ. Development	Caribbean
Environment	Latino/Hispanic
Education	Youth
Health Care	

FORT GREENE/CROWN HEIGHTS YOUTH SERVICE COALITION

215 Ryerson Street
Brooklyn, NY 11205

Phone: 718-636-5377
Fax: 718-636-8910
Contact: Frances Hanberry, VP
Marketing & Development

Office Hours: 9am-5pm
Staff: Paid
Geographic Scope: Brooklyn

Organizational Focus:
YSC attempts to address the vast and complicated array of educational, vocational, recreational and social services needs of inner city youth 5-24 years of age who reside throughout Brooklyn.

General Description:
YSC has provided a comprehensive array of human services to some of the borough's neediest and most at-risk children, adolescents and families.

Organizational Resources: Pamphlets
Membership Organization?: No

Issues:	Constituencies:
Education	African American
Youth	Latino/Hispanic
Anti-Violence	Youth

FOUNDATION FOR AFRICAN AMERICAN WOMEN

55 West 68th Street
New York, NY 10023

Phone: 212-799-0322
Contact: Antonia C. Martin

Office Hours: 9am-5pm
Staff: None
Geographic Scope: City-wide

Organizational Focus:
Women, philanthropy and social justice.

General Description:
A non-profit organization founded in 1990 concerned with the history and future of African American women. The foundation supports projects and initiatives of African American women and girls. We are proactive in the struggle for sexual and racial equity.

Organizational Resources: Brochure
Membership Organization?: No

Issues:	Constituencies:
Women's Rights	Women
Gender Issues	African American
Reproductive Rights	
Social Justice	

THE FREE SPIRIT

172 West 79th Street, Apt 8A
New York, NY 10024

Phone: 212-787-4643
Fax: Same/Call first
Contact: Roy Karp, Editor

Office Hours: 10am-6pm
Staff: None
Geographic Scope: Mostly
Manhattan

General Description:
Free Spirit is an independently
published, non-profit student
newspaper devoted to: peace, self-
government, freedom of speech,
equality and justice. More specifically
we support military disarmament,
alternative fuel sources such as solar
energy and hemp and local self
government. We are starting an
initiative to elect community boards
rather than have them appointed as is
done currently.

Organizational Resources:
Newsletter, newspaper space
available to give publicity to political
organizations holding rallies, forums,
petition drives, etc.
Regular Public Meetings: Yes
Membership Organization?: No

Issues:	Constituencies:
Social Justice	Multi Racial
Peace/Anti-Militarism	Youth
Election Reform	
Gov't Accountability	
Environment	

FRIENDS FOR JAMAICA

PO Box 20392 Park West Station
New York, NY 10025

E.Mail: <kitsond@mary.iia.org>
Contact: Rod Neyist

Office: No
Staff: Volunteer
Geographic Scope: City-wide

Organizational Focus:
Promoting the struggles of workers
in the Caribbean.

General Description:
Friends of Jamaica's main activity is
the publication of *Caribbean
Newsletter* (English-speaking
Caribbean). Covers economic,
political and social issues, as well as
arts and culture.

Organizational Resources: Caribbean
Newsletter

Issues:	Constituencies:
Human Rights	African American
Econ. Development	Caribbean
Arts/Culture	
Workers' Rights	

FUTURE LEADERS NETWORK

PO Box 170610
Brooklyn, NY 11217

Phone: 718-643-9603
Fax: Same
Contact: Ted Glick, Adult
Coordinator

Office Hours: 9am-6pm
Staff: Paid
Geographic Scope: City-wide

Organizational Focus:
Development of leadership skills and knowledge of teenage young people.

General Description:
Through meetings, conferences, a summer retreat, and a quarterly newsletter, we connect young people from 15 states who are organizers or who are learning to become one.

Organizational Resources:
Newsletter
Regular Public Meetings: Monthly
Membership Organization?: Yes
Membership Requirements:
Involvement in meetings and activities.

Issues:	Constituencies:
Youth & Students	Youth
Anti-Racism	
Women's Rights	
Education	
Social Justice	

GABRIELA NETWORK

PO Box 403, Times Sq. Station
New York, NY 10036-9998

Phone: 212-592-3507
Fax: 201-656-3970
Contact: Vivian Gupta, NY Chapter
Coordinator

Office: None
Staff: Volunteer
Geographic Scope: City-wide

Organizational Focus:
US and international policies which impact on women of the Philippines and women of Fil-Am origins.

General Description:
A Philippine-US women's solidarity organization.

Multi-lingual: Tagalog and Visayan

Organizational Resources:
Newsletter, pamphlets, speakers, and facilitators.
Regular Public Meetings: Every second and fourth Wednesday
Membership Organization?: Yes
Membership Requirements:
Orientation seminar; assigned tasks

Issues:	Constituencies:
Women's Rights	Seniors
Social Justice	Multi-Racial
Anti-Racism	
Anti-Violence	
Immigrants' Rights	
Int'l Solidarity	

A GATHERING OF THE TRIBES

285 East 3rd Street
New York, NY 10009

Phone: 212-674-3774
Fax: 212-674-5576
Contact: Steve Cannon, Director

Office Hours: Informal
Staff: Volunteer
Geographic Scope: City-wide

Organizational Focus:
A Gathering is a cross-generational diverse group of artists working together to create a better future.

Multi-lingual: Spanish, Hindi, German, Korean, Italian

Organizational Resources:
Computers, access to the internet and the space for rehearsal, workshops, Gallery.
Regular Public Meetings: First Saturday of month
Membership Organization?: No

Issues:
Arts/Culture
Education
Media

GAY & LESBIAN ALLIANCE AGAINST DEFAMATION (GLAAD)

150 West 26th Street, 503
New York, NY 10001

Phone: 212-807-1700
Fax: 212-807-1806
Contact: Cathay Che, Membership Director

Office Hours: 10am-6pm
Staff: Paid
Geographic Scope: National

Organizational Focus:
Works for more fair, accurate and inclusive representations of Lesbians, Gay men and bisexuals in media.

General Description:
GLAAD does its work through visibility and public education projects, media monitoring and response and media education.

Organizational Resources:
Newsletter, bulletin, weekly media activations - print, TV, phone hotline, speakers' bureau, media education seminars, video and print media archive, and a lesbian focus public access TV program.
Regular Public Meetings: 1st Wed of month 8pm. Center at 208 W. 13th St.
Membership Organization?: Yes
Membership Requirements: $35 annual dues, $10 for Bulletin only.

Issues:	Constituencies:
Media	Lesbian/Gay
Lesbian/Gay	Queers
Arts/Culture	Bisexuals
	Transgenders

GAY MEN OF THE BRONX (GMOB)

PO Box 511
Bronx, NY 10451

Phone: 718-378-3947
Contact: Ron Jacobowitz

Office?:   No
Staff: Volunteer
Geographic Scope: Bronx County

Organizational Focus:
To create a safe, supportive environment for Gay men who live in the Bronx and to advocate for their needs.

General Description:
GMOB is a multi-ethnic, multi-cultural organization, which provides social events, educational forums, rap sessions and encourages political action.

Bi-lingual: Spanish

Organizational Resources:
Newsletter
Regular Public Meetings: 1st Tuesday & 3rd Wednesday of month.
Membership Organization?: No

Issues: Constituencies:
Lesbian/Gay   Lesbian/Gay
Human Rights   Multi-Racial
HIV/AIDS   Latino/Hispanic
Social Justice

GAY MEN'S HEALTH CRISIS (GMHC)

129 West 20th Street
New York, NY 10011

Phone: 212-337-3353
Fax: 212-337-1220
Contact: Andy Stern, Public Policy
              Coordinator

Office Hours: 10am-6pm
Staff: Paid and volunteer
Geographic Scope: City-wide

Organizational Focus:
HIV/AIDS

General Description:
GMHC has a 3-point mission: to provide services for people living with HIV/AIDS; to prevent the spread of AIDS through education; and to advocate for greater government leadership and funding in order to provide better services and work toward both a vaccine and a cure.

Multi-lingual: Spanish, Svcs. for the hearing impaired

Organizational Resources:
Newsletters, forums on different topics several times a month, and information booklets.
Regular Public Meetings: Yes
Membership Organization?: No

Issues:
HIV/AIDS

GLOBAL KIDS

561 Broadway , 6th Floor
New York, NY 10012

Phone: 212-226-0130
Fax: 212-226-0137
Contact: Carole Nichols, Exec. Dir.

Office Hours: 9am-5pm
Staff: Paid and volunteer
Geographic Scope: City-wide

Organizational Focus:
Youth Development

General Description:
Global Kids is an independent non-
profit educational organization
dedicated to cultivating the knowledge, values, and leadership skills
necessary for young people to
address critical issues in their communities and to shape their future
lives in a culturally diverse world.

Multi-lingual: Spanish and French

Organizational Resources: Workshops, peer-led trainings and presentations, annual youth-led conference,
professional development for
educators and youth workers, youth-
produced videos.
Membership Organization?: No

Issues: Constituencies:
Youth   Youth
Anti-Racism   Multi-Racial
Anti-Violence   Students
Education   Educators
Human Rights
Leadership
Public Health

GODDARD RIVERSIDE COMMUNITY CENTER

593 Columbus Avenue
New York, NY 10024

Phone: 212-873-6600
Fax: 212-595-6498
Contact: Fannie Eisenstein,
          Education Coordinator

Office Hours: 9:00am-5:00pm
Staff: Paid
Geographic Scope: Manhattan's
Upper West Side

Organizational Focus:
Provisions of social services to
15,000 people a year of all ages and
racial and ethnic backgrounds.

General Description:
Goddard Riverside is a settlement
house that strives to involve its
diverse participants in realizing their
highest capacities through individual,
group and social action including
education, mobilization and mutual aid.

Multi-lingual: Spanish and Creole

Organizational Resources: Newsletter and limited meeting space.
Membership Organization?: Partially
Membership Requirements: Senior
Center has age and income requirements, Headstart and Day Care have
age, income, and need requirements.

Issues: Constituencies:
Youth   African American
Housing/   Multi-Racial
Homelessness   Latino/Hispanic
Students   Caribbean
Education   Seniors
                     Youth
                     Mentally Ill
                     Homeless

GODZILLA: ASIAN PACIFIC AMERICAN ART NETWORK

Cooper Station, PO Box 1116
New York, NY 10276

Phone: 212-228-6000 ext. 400
Fax: 212-966-8649
Contact: Todd Ayooung, Jenni Kim,
          Lynne Yamamoto,
          Steering Comm. members
Office: None
Staff: Volunteer
Geographic Scope: City-wide

General Description:
Godzilla is a New York based collective of Asian Pacific American artists, curators and writers. We function as a support group interested in social change through art, bringing together art and advocacy to increase visibility and opportunity for Asian Pacific Americans otherwise isolated with few resources. We contribute to changing the limited way Asian Pacific Americans participate in and are represented in society.

Organizational Resources:
Newsletter, slide registry of Asian Pacific American artists, speakers' bureau, workshop facilitators, curators and writers knowledgeable about Asian Pacific artists' concerns.
Regular Public Meetings: Bi-Monthly
Membership Organization?: No, but we do ask for small contribution to keep up our mailing list $5

Issues:	Constituencies:
Arts/Culture	Asian/Pacific
Education	Islander
Anti-Racism	
Immigrants' Rights	

GOOD OLD LOWER EAST SIDE (GOLES)

525 East 6th Street
New York, NY 10009

Phone: 212-533-2541
Fax: 212-533-8126
Contact: Donna G. Ellaby, Exec. Dir

Office Hours: Mon.-Fri. 10am-6pm
Staff: Paid and volunteer
Geographic Scope: Lower East Side; all of Community Board 3 area.

Organizational Focus:
Homelessness prevention and neighborhood preservation.

General Description:
GOLES has provided free housing-related technical assistance and advocacy to neighborhood residents for 17 years. GOLES aims to prevent displacement and homelessness by organizing tenants to become stronger advocates for their housing rights and by working with other community organizations to develop strategies for affordable, decent, integrated housing for the community.

Multi-lingual: Spanish, Ukrainian

Organizational Resources: Meet-ings on welfare reform, housing for people with HIV, lead paint poison-ing, workshops on tenants' rights.
Regular Public Meetings: Yes
Membership Organization?: No

Issues:	Constituencies:
Housing/	Multi-Racial
Homelessness	Seniors
Econ. Development	
Social Justice	
HIV/AIDS	

GOWANUS ARTS EXCHANGE INC.

295 Douglas Street
Brooklyn, NY 11217

Phone: 718-596-5250
Fax: 718-596-0051
Contact: Marya Warshaw, Exec Dir

Office Hours: Monday-Friday 9am
               6pm, Sat. 9am-1pm
Staff: Paid and Volunteer
Geographic Scope: Primarily
Brooklyn and city-wide

Organizational Focus:
Community arts.

General Description:
GAE is a not-for-profit community
arts organization. Included in its
focus are classes, workshops,
performances in dance, music and
theater. GAE provides performing
arts programs for area schools.

Organizational Resources: Meeting
space, workshop facilitators and
newsletter.
Regular Public Meetings: Call for
schedule
Membership Organization?: No

Issues:
Arts/Culture
Education
Youth
Media
Women's Rights

GREEN CORPS

c/o Audubon Society
700 Broadway, 5th Floor
New York, NY 10003

Phone: 212-979-3084
Fax: 212-353-0190
Contact: Alina Rocha, Environ-
          mental Organizer

Office Hours: Mon.-Fri. 9am-7pm
Staff: Volunteer
Geographic Scope: City-wide

Organizational Focus: Environmental
organizing. We organize students
and communities around different
environmental issues. We devote 6
to 8 weeks to each issue.

General Description:
At Green Corps, we organize and
mobilize students and the community
to work with us on environmental
campaigns which we develop for a
period of 6 to 8 weeks. In the past,
we have launched campaigns like the
Youth Vote '94, Boycott Mitsubishi,
and Energy Conservation.

Organizational Resources: Access to
many local environmental groups,
newsletter, student conferences.
Regular Public Meetings: Usually
every other Thursday night.

Issues: Constituencies:
Environment   High School/
Education   College Students
                     Multi-Racial

GREEN GUERRILLAS

625 Broadway, 2nd Floor
New York, NY 10012

Phone: 212-674-8124
Contact: Alison Blackman Dunham

Office Hours: 9am-5pm
Staff: Paid
Geographic Scope: City-wide

General Description:
22-year old 501(c)3) volunteer, non-profit dedicated to community gardening, urban greening, and environmental work. The GG's provide close to $300,000 in materials/plant donation and in technical assistance to 600 community gardens and 200 institutions in the city's 5 boroughs. The group also does special projects with diverse populations.

Bi-lingual: Spanish

Organizational Resources: Newsletter, workshops, speakers, composting, volunteer training and informational materials.
Regular Public Meetings: Quarterly
Membership Organization?: Yes
Membership Requirements: Dues and/or volunteer work.

Issues:
Environment
Arts/Culture
Gov't Accountability
Education
Econ. Development

GREENPEACE

462 Broadway, 6th Floor
New York, NY 10013

Phone: 212-941-0994
Fax: 212-941-1928
Contact: Alison Holden, Resource
          Staff

Office Hours: 9am-5pm
Staff: Paid
Geographic Scope: City-wide

Organizational Focus:
Greenpeace is an international organization dedicated to preserving the earth and all the life it supports.

General Description:
GP works on the following issues: nuclear and toxic pollution, nuclear weapons, global warming, ozone layer destruction and ocean ecology. We use education, outreach, lobbying, non-violent direct action, media and research as tools to change public and private policy.

Organizational Resources:
Newsletter
Membership Organization?: Yes

Issues:
Environment

HAITI ANTI-INTERVENTION COMMITTEE

PO Box 755 Fort Washington Sta.
New York, NY 10040

Phone: 212-592-3612
Contact: Marty Goodman

Office?: No
Staff: None
Geographic Scope: City-wide

Organizational Focus:
Oppose intervention and support
popular movements in Haiti.

General Description:
We are an activist oriented
committee that produces educational
literature and organizes protests.

Multi-lingual: French, Creole

Organizational Resources:
Literature, speakers and videos
Membership Organization?: No

Issues: Constituencies:
Int'l Solidarity   Caribbean
Human Rights   Multi-Racial
Peace/Anti Militarism
Anti-Racism
Immigrants' Rights

HAITI SOLIDARITY NETWORK

202 East 32nd Street
Brooklyn, NY 11226

Phone: 718-856-5277
Fax: 718-284-5320
Contact: Jean D. Vernet, II,
          Director

Office?: No
Staff: Volunteer
Geographic Scope: City-wide

Organizational Focus:
To facilitate the integration of the
Haitian American community, and
support democracy in Haiti.

General Description:
Started in January 1991, the network
offers limited citizenship services;
organizes workshops on issues
relevant to Haitian Americans such
as: how to vote and African
American history, and conducts
leadership and organizational
workshops.

Multi-lingual: French, Haitian Creole

Organizational Resources:
Speakers' bureau on Haitian issues
and workshop facilitators.
Membership Organization?: Yes
Membership Requirements: Support
goals

Issues: Constituencies:
Human Rights   Haitian
Immigrants' Rights   Caribbean
Int'l Solidarity   African American
Voting Rights
Workers' Rights

HAITIAN INFORMATION AND DOCUMENTATION CENTER

1218 Flatbush Avenue
Brooklyn, NY 11226

Phone: 718-284-0889
Fax: 718-284-2545
Contact: Daniel Huttinot, President

Office Hours: 12-9:30pm
Staff: Volunteer
Geographic Scope: East Flatbush

Organizational Focus:
Haitian community center.

General Description:
The Haitian Information and Documentation Center offers services as varied as English and Creole lessons or tutoring and referral services on issues of Immigrants' Rights.

Multi-lingual: Creole, French

Regular Public Meetings: Yes
Membership Organization?: No

Issues:	Constituencies:
Education	Caribbean
Human Rights	Multi-Racial
Immigrants' Rights	
Legal	
Media	

HARLEM BIRTH ACTION COMMITTEE

2472 Frederick Douglass Blvd.
New York, NY 10027

Phone: 212-694-1929
Fax: 212-862-0644
Contact: Nonkululeko Tyehemba,
            Director or Twana Adams,
            Coor.

Office Hours: Tuesday-Saturday
Staff: Volunteer
Geographic Scope: Harlem

Organizational Focus:
Combating: infant mortality, low birth weight, the high incidence of late or no prenatal care, and high percentage of caesarean sections performed during child birth.

General Description:
HBAC provides workshops, seminars, conferences and support groups for expecting parents in the Harlem community. The committee conducts birth classes for families, support groups for pregnant women, referrals, community baby showers.

Multi-lingual:Spanish, French, Woloff

Organizational Resources: Newsletter, meeting space, pamphlets, and film festivals on health issues.
Membership Organization?: Yes
Membership Requirements: Interest in goals

Issues:	Constituencies:
Health Care	Women
Reproductive Rights	Youth
Women's Rights	African American
Youth	Caribbean
	Latino/Hispanic

HARLEM ENVIRONMENTAL IMPACT PROJECT, INC.

c/o ACP, Jr. State Office Bldg.
163 West 125 St. Suite 909
New York, NY 10027

Phone: 212-749-5298
Fax: 212-749-3745
Contact: Gregory Mills, Chair

Office Hours: Mon.-Fri. 9am-5pm
Staff: Volunteer
Geographic Scope: Harlem

Organizational Focus:
To identify and resolve environmental health hazards facing the entire Harlem community.

General Description:
Through public information and educational campaigns to address solid waste reduction, the North River Sewage Treatment Plant, recycling, conservation, ecology, asbestos, lead poisoning, air pollution, transportation and other health concerns.

Bi-lingual: Spanish

Organizational Resources:
Newsletters, seminars, conferences, workshops, videos.
Regular Public Meetings: Yes
Membership Organization?: Yes
Membership Requirements: Reside or work in Harlem

Issues: Constituencies:
Environment   African American
Education   Latino/Hispanic
Social Justice
Legal

HELL'S KITCHEN AIDS PROJECT, INC.

328 West 48th Street
New York, NY 10036

Phone: 212-956-7587
Fax: Same/Call first
Contact: Michael Tucker, Exec. Dir.

Office?:   Yes
Staff: Paid and volunteer

Organizational Focus:
HIV/AIDS Education

General Description:
Hell's Kitchen AIDS Project, Inc. (HKAP) is a non-profit organization committed to educating a diverse group of youth about HIV and AIDS. Using the arts as a vehicle for education, HKAP attempts to reduce the incidence of HIV infection.
Geographic Scope: Chelsea/Clinton

Bi-lingual: Spanish (some staff)

Organizational Resources:
HIV/AIDS peer educators, art related.
Membership Organization?: No

Issues: Constituencies:
Education   Multi-Racial
HIV/AIDS   Youth
Human Rights   Lesbian/Gay
Arts/Culture

H.E.L.P. BRONX, INC.

285 East 171st Street
Bronx, NY 10457

Phone: 718-583-0174
Fax: 718-583-9085
Contact: Henry Beattie, Director of
          Program Services

Office Hours: 24 hours a day
Staff: Paid
Geographic Scope: Bronx, Brooklyn,
& Manhattan

Organizational Focus:
Housing

General Description:
Our main function is to serve as the
country's largest organization that
operates Tier II homeless shelters.
In addition we organize against
budget cuts and advocate for housing
for the homeless.

Multi-lingual: Spanish

Organizational Resources:
Newsletter
Membership Organization?: No

Issues: Constituencies:
Housing/   Multi-Racial
Homelessness

HENRY STREET SETTLEMENT ABRONS ARTS CENTER

466 Grand Street
New York, NY 10002

Phone: 212-598-0400
Fax: 212-505-8329
Contact: Jonathon Ward, Program
          Associate

Office Hours: 10am-6pm
Staff: Paid
Geographic Scope: Lower East Side

General Description:
We are a community based arts
organization which offers classes and
workshops as well as performances
in dance, drama, music and exhibits.
We have three theaters, an
amphitheater, art galleries, studios,
and rehearsal spaces. Classes and
workshops are for all ages and skill
levels.

Multi-lingual: Spanish and Chinese

Organizational Resources: Newsletter, performances, speakers,
meeting space, and brochures about
programs.
Membership Organization?: No

Issue:
Arts/Culture

HETRICK-MARTIN INSTITUTE

2 Astor Place
New York, NY 10003

Phone: 212 674-2400
Fax: 212-674-8650
Contact: Lissette Cheng,
          Administrative Asst.

Office Hours: Mon.-Fri. 8am-8pm
Staff: Paid and volunteer
Geographic Scope: City-wide

Organizational Focus:
Meeting the needs of Lesbian, Gay
and Bisexual youth, homeless
adolescents, and all youth who are
coming to terms with sexuality. The
institute also emphasizes HIV/AIDS
education.

General Description:
Hetrick-Martin provides counseling,
training, advocacy and leadership
programs

Bi-lingual: Spanish

Organizational Resources:
Newsletter, booklets, brochures,
pamphlets, speakers' bureaus,
workshop facilitators, hotline,
posters, directories, comic books,
and resource files.
Membership Organization?: Yes
Membership Requirements: Free
membership for people between the
ages of 12 and 21.

Issues: Constituencies:
Youth   Youth
Lesbian/Gay   Lesbian/Gay
Education   Bisexual/
HIV/AIDS   Transgender

HOUSING CONSERVATION COORDINATORS (HCC)

777 10th Avenue
New York, NY 10019

Phone: 212-541-5996
Fax: 212-541-5966
Contact: Kyle E. Stewart, Exec. Dir.

Office Hours: 9am-5pm +
Staff: Paid
Geographic Scope: Clinton
neighborhood of Manhattan

Organizational Focus:
Homelessness prevention and
neighborhood stabilization through
tenants' rights advocacy and technical
assistance.

General Description:
HCC is a 22 year old CBO providing
6 related programs to preserve the
working class composition of the
Clinton (Hell's Kitchen) neighborhood of NYC including: weatheriza-
tion, loan funds for building repair,
technical training in home repair, 7a
administration, food for senior
citizens program and legal and tenant
organizing.

Multi-lingual: Spanish, French

Organizational Resources:
Meeting space, workshop facilitators
in fundraising and housing issues.
Membership Organization?: No

Issues: Constituencies:
Housing/   Multi-Racial
Homelessness   African American
Legal   Latino/Hispanic
Social Justice

HOUSING SOLIDARITY NETWORK

674 East 136th Street, Apt. B
Bronx, NY 10454

Phone: 718-292-6443
Contact: Elizabeth Batiuk, Legal
           Comm. Coordinator

Office Hours: Call for times
Staff: Volunteer
Geographic Scope: City-wide

Organizational Focus:
Housing. Organizing a City-wide rent strike and other forms of direct action to address the housing crisis.

General Description:
Has provided technical assistance to tenants, squatters, homeless people and peddlers. Including: legal support, project and tenant organizers' training and lead paint poisoning rights orientations.

Organizational Resources:
Newsletter, housing organizer seminars, technical assistance to tenant associations.
Regular Public Meetings: Yes
Membership Organization?: Yes
Membership Requirements:
Volunteer on one of the committees

Issues: Constituencies:
Housing   Tenants
Homelessness   Homeless
Social Justice   People
                     Squatters
                     Peddlers

HUDSON GUILD

441 West 26th Street
New York, NY 10001

Phone: 212-760-9804
Fax: 212-268-9983
Contact: Janice McGuire, Exec. Dir.

Office Hours: Mon.-Fri. 8am-6pm
Staff: Paid and volunteer
Geographic Scope: Chelsea

Organizational Focus:
HG is a multi-service settlement house working to provide services to enhance Manhattan's Chelsea community.

General Description:
In addition to a wide variety of direct services, the Guild works to facilitate and support community improvement efforts.

Bi-lingual: Spanish

Organizational Resources:
Meeting space with priority given to local groups.
Membership Organization?: Yes
Membership Requirements: Fee $5-$24 Annually

HUMAN SERVE

622 West 113th Street Rm. 410
New York, NY 10025

Phone: 212-854-4053
Fax: 212-854-8727
Contact: Louise Altman, NY Dir.
          David Plotkin, Office Mgr.

Office Hours: 9am-5pm
Staff: Paid
Geographic Scope: City-wide and national

Organizational Focus:
Enforcement of the national voter registration act in all fifty states.

General Description:
Human Serve is a national, non-partisan voter registration and voting rights advocacy organization.

Bi-lingual: Spanish

Organizational Resources:
Newsletter, clearinghouse for information on our issue.
Membership Organization?: No

Issues:
Voting Rights

HUNGER ACTION NETWORK OF NEW YORK STATE

115 East 23rd Street, 10th Fl.
New York, NY 10010

Phone: 212-505-2055
Fax: 212-674-1946
Contact: Paul Getsos, Downstate
          Director

Office Hours: 9am-6pm
Staff: Paid and volunteer
Geographic Scope: New York State

Organizational Focus:
To end hunger and poverty in New York State and to develop leadership in low income communities.

General Description:
Through public education outreach, community organizing and empowering low income New Yorkers, HANNYS works to end hunger. HANNYS helps low income people organize on their own behalf to impact on local, state and federal policy issues.

Organizational Resources: Newsletter, speakers and workshops and technical assistance in community organizing.
Regular Public Meetings: Yes
Membership Organization?: Yes

Issues:	Constituencies:
Social Justice	Low Income
Welfare Advocacy	People on
Gov't Accountability	Welfare
	Multi-Racial
	Homeless people

IDENTITY HOUSE

PO Box 572, Old Chelsea Sta.
New York, NY 10011

Phone: 212-243-0423
Contact: Kay Lockridge, Exec. Dir.

Office Hours: Sunday, Monday &
                Tuesday 6am-10pm
Staff: Volunteer
Geographic Scope: City-wide

Organizational Focus:
We are a peer counseling and
therapy referral center for the
lesbian, gay and bisexual community.

General Description:
We offer rap groups, short-term
groups, workshops and special events
for the community.

Organizational Resources:
Speakers' Bureau
Regular Public Meetings: Yes
Friday from 6:30-8:30pm and
Saturday from 3-5pm are women's
meetings. Men's meetings are from
8:30-10:30pm on Friday and from 3-
5pm on Sunday.
Membership Organization?: Yes
Membership Requirements: $75 year,
must be at least 18 years old.

Issues: Constituencies:
Lesbian/Gay   Lesbian/Gay

IFCO: THE INTER-RELIGIOUS FOUNDATION FOR COMMUNITY ORGANIZATIONS

402 West 145th Street
New York, NY 10031

Phone: 212-926-5757
Fax: 212-926-5842
Contact: Ellen Bernstein, Grants
           Administrator

Office Hours: 10am-6pm
Staff: Paid
Geographic Scope: City-wide and
national

Organizational Focus:
IFCO is a multi-issue agency that
organizes for racial, social, and
economic justice.

General Description:
The first national foundation controlled
by people of color, IFCO has initiated,
advised and supported hundreds of
community based organizations. IFCO
offers TA and training to grassroots
projects. IFCO's international work
includes Pastors for Peace/US-Cuba
friendshipment caravans.

Bi-lingual: Spanish

Organizational Resources: Speakers
and workshop facilitators on Cuba;
videos of friendship caravans.
Program planning/proposal writing
workshops. Conferences and
networking. Fiscal agency services.

Issues: Constituencies:
Social Justice   Multi-Racial
Human Rights   Women
                       Lesbian/Gay

ILLUSION PRODUCTIONS
135 Prospect Park West, Ste. 24B
Brooklyn, New York 11215

Phone: 718-499-5342
Fax: 718-499-2216
Contact: Wendy Weiss, Director

Staff: Volunteer
Geographic Scope: City-wide

Organizational Focus:
AIDS and adolescents.

General Description:
Illusion Productions uses dance and
music as a vehicle for AIDS education
by and for young people in New
York City.

Multi-lingual: Spanish and American
Sign Language

Organizational Resources: AIDS
education performances
Membership Organization?:No

Issues:	Constituencies:
HIV/AIDS	Multi-Cultural
Arts/Culture	Multi-Racial
Education	Lesbian/Gay
Students	Youth

IMMIGRANTS' THEATRE PROJECT, INC.
44 Douglass Street
Brooklyn, NY 11231

Phone: 718-237-4545
Contact: Marcy Arlin, Artistic Dir.

Office Hours: Call & leave message
Staff: Paid and volunteer
Geographic Scope: City-wide

Organizational Focus:
Write, perform, and produce plays
about immigrant experience, past and
present in the US. Promote
interethnic understanding through
the arts.

General Description:
Theatre ensemble with artists from
over 15 ethnic and national groups.
We produce new plays either by
immigrants or with themes relating
to immigrants.

Multi-lingual: Members speak a
variety of different languages

Organizational Resources:
Workshop: dramatizing family
histories, role-playing techniques for
intercultural communication. Small
performances and a professional,
annual new immigrant play series in
Brooklyn.
Membership Organization?: No

Issues:	Constituencies:
Arts/Culture	Multi-Racial
Immigrants' Rights	Multi-Cultural

INFORM, INC.

120 Wall Street, 16th Floor
New York, NY 10005

Phone: 212-361-2400
Fax: 212-361-2412
E-mail: Inform@igc.apc.org
Contact: Joanna Underwood,
           President

Office Hours: Mon.-Fri. 9am-5pm
Staff: Paid

Geographic Scope: National
Organizational Focus:
Waste and pollution prevention
research and advocacy.

General Description:
INFORM reports on issues of
pollution prevention, waste
reduction at the source, alternative
transportation energy fuels. INFORM
conducts outreach to communities,
municipalities and businesses.

Multi-lingual: We have various
international outreach programs

Organizational Resources:
INFORM reports and newsletter.
Membership Organization?: Yes
Membership Requirements:
Contributory

Issues: Constituencies:
Environment   Multi-Racial

INGERSOLL TENANT ASSOCIATION, INC.

173 Myrtle Avenue - Grd. Floor
Brooklyn, NY 11201

Phone: 718-875-6043
Fax: 718-858-5249
Contact: Michael E. Boyd, Exec. Dir.

Office Hours: Mon.-Fri. 9am-5pm &
              Saturday 10am-2pm
Staff: Paid and volunteer
Geographic Scope: Ingersoll, Brooklyn

Organizational Focus:
Service and social action

General Description:
Non-profit community based multi-
services center with programs for
youth, young adults and seniors.
Programs range from photo club,
mentor, martial arts and dance, youth
community library, 12-step recovery
and information and referral.

Bi-lingual: Spanish

Organizational Resources:
AIDS/HIV bureau, youth conflict
resolution, seminars, speakers'
exchange on social issues.
Regular Public Meetings: Last
Monday every month
Membership Organization?: Yes
Membership Requirements:
Residents of Ingersoll public housing.

Issues: Constituencies:
Social Justice   Multi-Racial
Economic Equality   African American
                     Latino/Hispanic

INNER CITY PRESS

PO Box 416, Hub Station
Bronx, NY 10455

Phone: 718-716-3540
Fax: 718-716-3161
Contact: Matthew Lee, Exec. Dir.

Office?:   Yes
Staff: Paid
Geographic Scope: City-wide

General Description:
We are a group based in the South
Bronx, serving Upper Manhattan as
well, which focuses on the lack of
housing, the lack of accountability,
and the lack of access to credit and
opportunity here. We do home-
steading (homeless and underhoused
people repairing abandoned buildings), tenant organizing, publish a
bilingual, bimonthly newspaper with a
circulation of 32,000; challenge banks
who are redlining neighborhoods,
testify about corrupt deals here.

Bi-lingual: Spanish

Organizational Resources:
Newspaper, pamphlets on housing
court, occupants rights
Regular Public Meetings: Yes
Membership Organization?: No

Issues:	Constituencies:
Housing/Homeless	Multi-Racial
Gov't Accountability	Latino/Hispanic
Media	
Legal	
Econ. Development	

INNOVATIVE COMMUNITY ENTERPRISES

209 East 10th Street, Apt. 10
New York, NY 10003

Phone: 212-529-8200
Fax: 212-420-0915
Contact: Seth Appel, Exec. Director

Office Hours: 9:30am-5:00pm +
Staff: Paid

Organizational Focus:
Solving difficult social and economic
problems with replicable projects.
We deal with social problems by
defining and then addressing them.

General Description:
We work in schools, senior centers,
and homeless shelters with groups of
five to thirty on issues of conflict
prevention and intergroup
connections.

Multi-lingual: Spanish, German,
Russian

Organizational Resources:
Newsletter. We welcome
applications for free space at our fair,
the more the exhibitor/presenter
involves his/her audience, the more
likely we will offer free space.
Regular Public Meetings: Weekly fair
at 11 & 12th St. between 1-2pm.
Membership Organization?: No

Issues:	Constituencies:
Social Justice	Youth
Anti-Violence	Seniors
Education	Multi-Racial
Econ. Development	Youth

INSTITUTE FOR PUERTO RICAN POLICY (IPR)

286 Fifth Avenue, 3rd Floor
New York, NY 10001-4512

Phone: 212-564-1075
Fax: 212-564-1014
Contact: Angelo Falcon, President

Office Hours: 9am-5pm
Staff: Volunteer and Paid
Geographic Scope: City-wide

Organizational Focus:
Non-profit, non-partisan policy center focusing on Puerto Rican and other Latino community issues.

General Description:
Specializing in guerrilla research, IPR focuses on policy analysis, civic participation and policy networking. Our approach combines technical with political aspects of the policy process.

Bi-lingual: Spanish

Organizational Resources:
Publications on Puerto Rican issues, such as monthly *Critica: A Journal of Puerto Rican Politics and Policy*; annual *Soy Boricua!*; *Dialogo* newsletter, reports and an activist calendar.
Regular Public Meetings: Bimonthly and annual fundraising dance
Membership Requirements: Interest in community issues

Issues: Constituencies:
Gov't Accountability   Puerto Rican
Social Justice   Latino/Hispanic
Voting Rights   Multi-Racial
Anti-Racism
Media

INTERFAITH ASSEMBLY ON HOMELESSNESS AND HOUSING

1047 Amsterdam Avenue
New York, NY 10025

Phone: 212-316-3171
Fax: 212-932-7348
Contact: Marc L. Greenberg, Exec. Director

Office Hours: 9:30am-6pm
Staff: Paid
Geographic Scope: City-wide

Organizational Focus:
To assist homeless people in their recovery from the trauma associated with homelessness and to change public perception and policy through their public speaking and participation in activities.

General Description:
A coalition of religious organizations and housed and homeless people offering life skills classes, public presentations and organizing public events and campaigns.

Organizational Resources:
Speakers' bureau of formerly homeless men and women.
Regular Public Meetings: Yes
Membership Requirements: Religious Institution

Issues:
Housing/Homelessness
Social Justice
Education

INTERNATIONAL ACTION CENTER

39 West 14th Street, Ste. 206
New York, NY 10011

Phone: 212-633-6646
Fax: 212-633-2889
Contact: Deirdre Sinnott

Office Hours: 10am-7pm
Staff: Volunteer
Geographic Scope: City-wide

Organizational Focus:
The IAC is a multi-national, multi-issue volunteer organization with many organizational affiliates.

General Description:
We are an anti-racist, pro-choice, pro-lesbian/gay/bisexual and transgender liberation, anti-US imperialism organization. We fight for jobs at a decent wage for all and against immigrant bashing.

Organizational Resources:
Videos, books, and speakers.
Regular Public Meetings: Monthly forum & weekly volunteer meetings.
Membership Organization?: No

Issues:	Constituencies:
Peace/	Multi-Racial
Anti-Militarism	Youth
Anti-Racism	Lesbian/Gay
Social Justice	
Int'l Solidarity	

INTERNATIONAL AGENCY FOR MINORITY ARTIST AFFAIRS

ACP, Jr. State Office Building
163 W. 125 Street, Suite 909
New York, NY 10027

Phone: 212-749-5298
Fax: 212-749-3745
Contact: Gregory Mills, Chair/CEO

Office Hours: Mon.-Fri. 9am-5pm
Staff: Paid and volunteer
Geographic Scope: City-wide

Organizational Focus:
To provide resources, training and exposure for artists of color.

General Description:
Operate the art gallery of the State office building; publishes *Uptown Art News*, sponsors the annual state of the arts conference, offers non-profit management training for artists and organizations, presents ongoing film festivals and seminars.

Multi-lingual: Spanish

Organizational Resources: Newsletter, speakers, workshops, conferences, meeting space, consultants.
Membership Organization?: Yes
Membership Requirements: Be an artist of color or work for an arts or cultural organization serving communities of color.

Issues:	Constituencies:
Arts/Culture	Women
Education	Multi-Racial
Gov't	Senior
Accountability	All people of
HIV/AIDS	color
Media	

INTERNATIONAL PEACE FOR CUBA APPEAL

39 West 14th Street, #206
New York, NY 10011

Phone: 212-633-6646
Fax: 212-633-2889
Contact: Teresa Gutierrez, Dir.

Office Hours: 10am-7pm
Staff: Volunteer
Geographic Scope: City-wide

Organizational Focus:
To show solidarity with the Cuban
people; to organize against US
embargo and military threats against
Cuba; to raise material aid; and, to
educate the US people about Cuba.

General Description:
Activist organization which holds
meetings, rallies, demonstrations, and
more to counter US aggression
against Cuba and to show solidarity
with Cuban people.

Bi-lingual: Spanish

Organizational Resources: Newsletter, pamphlets, videos, speakers'
bureau, workshop facilitators.
Regular Public Meetings: Yes
Membership Organization?: No

Issues: Constituencies:
Int'l Solidarity   Multi-Racial
Peace/Anti-Militarism
Anti-Racism

IRISH LESBIAN & GAY ORGANIZATION (ILGO)

208 West 13th Street
New York, NY 10011

Phone: 212-967-7711 Ext 3078
Contact: John Francis Mulligan

Office?:   No
Staff: None
Geographic Scope: City-wide

General Description:
Social, cultural and political group for
Irish and Irish American Lesbians and
Gay men.

Organizational Resources:
Newsletter and hotline.
Membership Organization?: No

Issues: Constituencies:
Lesbian/Gay   Lesbian/Gay
Social Justice   Irish
Education

IT'S TIME...INC.
139 Henry Street
New York, NY 10002

Phone: 212-962-3069
Fax: 212-406-5879
Contact: Tony Johnson, Exec. Dir.

Office Hours: Mon.-Fri. 9am-5pm
Staff: Paid
Geographic Scope: Lower Manhattan, however Chinese-speaking clients come from all 5 boroughs.

Organizational Focus:
Tenants' rights and community empowerment in the Lower East Side and Chinatown.

General Description:
Multi-ethnic CBO engaged in tenant organizing, individual housing and senior services, youth center programs and homeless housing development.

Multi-lingual: Spanish, Cantonese, Fukinese, Mandarin and Toishan

Organizational Resources:
Chinese and Spanish tenants' rights brochures, small meeting space, tenants' rights workshop (tri-lingual) and a youth center newsletter.
Regular Public Meetings: 2-4 evening per year
Membership Organization?: No

Issues: Constituencies:
Housing/   Multi-Racial
Homelessness
Immigrants' Rights
Seniors
Youth

JAPANESE AMERICAN SOCIAL SERVICES, INC. (JASSI)
275 Seventh Avenue, 21st Floor
New York, NY 10001

Phone: 212-255-1881
Fax: 212-255-3281
Contact: Cyril Nishimoto, Director

Office Hours: Monday-Friday 10am-
                    5:30pm
Staff: Paid
Geographic Scope: City-wide

Organizational Focus:
JASSI enables people of Japanese ancestry in need to overcome linguistic, cultural, racial, and geographical barriers, and gain access to social services.

General Description:
JASSI helps resolve problems related to government benefits, housing, immigration, domestic violence, health, and consumer rights; informs the community about services; conducts a program for seniors.

Bi-lingual: Japanese

Organizational Resources:
Monthly service news bulletins, quarterly newsletter, speakers on Japanese American internment camp experience during World War II.
Membership Organization?: No

Issues: Constituencies:
Social Justice   Asian/Pacific
Immigrants' Rights   Islander
Seniors

JEWS FOR RACIAL & ECONOMIC JUSTICE

64 Fulton Street, No 605
New York, NY 10038

Phone: 212-964-9210
Fax: 212-964-9275
Contact: Melanie Kaye/Kantrowitz,
          Executive Director

Office Hours: Mon.-Fri. afternoons
Staff: Paid
Geographic Scope: City-wide

General Description:
We raise issues of race and class in the Jewish community, work to strengthen and enlarge the community of activist Jews, counter the claim of conservatives to speak for all Jews by asserting a strong progressive Jewish voice, and bring a Jewish presence to justice-seeking coalitions.

Organizational Resources:
Speakers, newsletter with a calendar, workshop facilitators, pamphlets, and people-support for coalitions
Regular Public Meetings: Monthly coffeehouse meeting.
Membership Organization?: Yes
Membership Requirements: $36, Low Income $9

Issues: Constituencies:
Anti-Racism   Jewish
Social Justice
Workers' Rights
Lesbian/Gay
Women's Rights

A JOB IS A RIGHT CAMPAIGN

39 West 14th Street, Rm. 206
New York, NY 10011

Phone: 212-633-6646
Fax: 212-633-2889
Contact: Greg Butterfield,
          Volunteer Organizer

Office Hours: Mon.-Sat. 10am-8pm
Staff: Volunteer
Geographic Scope: City-wide, but also connected nationwide with chapters in over 25 cities.

Organizational Focus:
Fighting for jobs, decent wages and union rights for all.

General Description:
Organize poor and working people of all nationalities to fight for their right to jobs and income. Sponsor demonstrations, picket lines, educational meetings, press conferences and other activities.

Multi-lingual: Spanish, Creole and others

Organizational Resources:
Newsletter, pamphlets, fact sheets, videos, speakers
Regular Public Meetings: Yes
Membership Organization?: No

Issues: Constituencies:
Workers' Rights   Multi-Racial
Welfare Advocacy   Lesbian/Gay
Int'l Solidarity   Youth
Youth   Women

KENSINGTON ACTION FORCE

4520 18th Avenue
Brooklyn, NY 11204

Phone: 718-435-1300
Fax: 718-282-8913
Contact: Sidney Zelman,
           Coordinator/Director

Office?:   Yes
Staff: Paid
Geographic Scope: Kensington, Brooklyn

Organizational Focus:
To upgrade the quality of life for residents in Kensington through a combination of community and statewide educational efforts .

General Description:
16,000-64,000 community residents benefit from a host of programs such as volunteer community patrol, meetings with police, elected officials, community board to demand attention to the community.

Multi-lingual: Russian, Yiddish, Spanish

Organizational Resources:
Newsletter and presently developing a national community safety expo.
Regular Public Meetings: 4x's a year: March, May, Sept. & November
Membership Organization?: Yes
Membership Requirements: Live in Kensington/$25

Issues: Constituencies:
Crime/   All Kensington
Criminal Justice   residents
Education
Anti-Violence

KIDS MEETING KIDS

350 Riverside Drive
New York, NY 10025

Phone: 212-662-2327
Fax: 212-222-1416
Contact: Herbert Williams, Youth
           Organizer

Office Hours: After school & evenings
Staff: Paid and volunteer
Geographic Scope: City-wide

Organizational Focus:
Peace, justice and children's rights

General Description:
Kids Meeting Kids is a youth-run organization involving kids ages 5 to 19 from many backgrounds and cultures. We work locally, nationally and internationally to bring peace and fairness to all kids.

Organizational Resources:
Newsletters, videos, speakers' bureau, workshop facilitators & special program "Days Against Violence."
Regular Public Meetings: Fridays at 4pm
Membership Organization?: Yes
Membership Requirements: Being active in organization's activities.

Issues: Constituencies:
Human Rights   Youth
Social Justice   Students
Peace/   Multi-Racial
Anti-Militarism
Anti-Violence
Anti-Racism

KOREAN AMERICAN FAMILY SERVICE CENTER

PO Box 20202
New York, NY 10001

Phone: 212-465-0664
Fax: Same
Contact: Jiyoung Kim, Exec. Dir.

Office Hours: M,W,F. 9am-5pm,
                      Tu.,Thurs. 9-8pm
Staff: Paid
Geographic Scope: City-wide

Organizational Focus:
Family services for Korean Americans
with priority given to domestic
violence intervention/prevention

General Description:
Family support programs for
divorced mothers; emotionally
disturbed children; family counseling

Bi-lingual: Korean

Organizational Resources:
Pamphlets/Brochures available and
newsletter
Membership Organization?: No

Issues: Constituencies:
Women's Rights   Asian/Pacific
Anti-Violence   Islander
Anti-Racism

KOREAN AMERICANS FOR SOCIAL CONCERN

PO Box 7253
Flushing, NY 11352

Phone: 718-651-9077
Contact: Jay Sung Lee

Office?:   No
Staff: None
Geographic Scope: City-wide

Organizational Focus:
Korean Americans living in the NYC
area.

General Description:
KASC is a community-based
organization/ advocacy group. It
seeks to serve as a bridge between
the Korean community and the larger
American community. Past and
current projects include voter
registration, 1990 census, coalition
work with other organizations and
education on Black/Korean conflict.

Bi-lingual: Korean

Regular Public Meetings: Monthly
Membership Organization?: Yes

Issues: Constituencies:
Social Justice   Asian/Pacific
Anti-Racism   Islander
Anti-Violence
Crime/Criminal Justice
Education

LA ASOCIACION BENEFICA CULTURAL FATHER BILLINI

104-11 37th Avenue
Corona, NY 11368

Phone: 718-651-8427
Fax: 718-651-5572
Contact: Ana Lopez, Exec. Director

Office Hours: 9-6 pm
Staff: None
Geographic Scope: City-wide

Organizational Focus:
Provides services to NYC residents
particularly at-risk youth,
economically disadvantaged and
limited English-proficiency individuals.

General Description:
A non-profit, city-wide, multi-service
organization. Lead agency of
Claridad Beacon school, a school-
based community center that
expands neighborhood access to
positive programs. It provides a wide
array of educational, recreational,
vocational, counseling and referral
services.

Bi-lingual: Spanish

Organizational Resources:
Meeting Space
Regular Public Meetings: Yes   Every
3 Months
Membership Organization?: No

Issues: Constituencies:
Youth   Youth
Arts/Culture   Latino/Hispanic
                      Multi-Racial

LABOR AT THE CROSSROADS

695 Park Ave. Rm. 340n
New York, NY 10021

Phone: 212-772-4129
Fax: 212-772-4088
Contact: Simin Farkhondeh

Office Hours: Tues., Thur, and
               Friday 10am-6pm
Staff: Paid
Geographic Scope: City-wide

General Description:
Labor X is a video/television program
designed to put working people's
voices and the issues important to
them on TV. Each 30-minute show
provides up-to-date information and
strategies for organizing around
important issues, such as national
health care, labor, education, and
housing. Video tapes are shown on
CUNY TV public access.

Organizational Resources:
We provide videotapes as organizing
tools at affordable prices. We are
currently working towards making
workers' video training workshops
available. We broadcast our program
on CUNY TV, channel 75.
Membership Organization?: No

Issues: Constituencies:
Workers' Rights   Working People
Labor
Social Justice
Anti-Racism

LABOR MILITANT

PO Box 5442
Long Island City, NY 11105

Phone: 718-956-7753
Fax: 718-956-7748
Contact: Alan Akrivos

Office?: No
Staff: Volunteer
Geographic Scope: National

Organizational Focus:
Trade unionists, workers, youth and women.

General Description:
Labor Militant is a newspaper that fights against inequality, racism, poverty and the alienation of capitalist society. We fight for socialism in the US and abroad. Groups of supporters campaign for these ideas in the labor movement, among the working class and youth.

Bi-lingual: Spanish

Organizational Resources:
Pamphlets, newspaper, speakers
Membership Organization?: Yes

Membership Requirements:
Subscribe to magazine and participate in discussion groups.

Issues:	Constituencies:
Socialism	Working Class
Social Justice	
Workers' Rights	

LATIN AMERICAN WOMEN'S NETWORK

611 West 177 Street, Suite 5
New York, NY 10033

Phone: 212-927-2800
Fax: 212-927-8548
Contact: Esmeralda Diaz, Exec. Dir.

Office Hours: 9am-6pm
Staff: Paid
Geographic Scope: City-wide

Organizational Focus:
Education, counseling and referrals.

General Description:
LAWN is a direct response to community needs: an organization initiated, designed, and maintained by Latinas in Washington Heights. LAWN runs programs including GED, math and English classes, as well as workshops on community empowerment. Through LAWN, community members are able to share ideas and coordinate activities with other NY Hispanic organizations.

Bi-lingual: Spanish

Membership Organization?: No

Issues:	Constituencies:
Education	Women
Int'l Solidarity	Latino/Hispanic
Women's Rights	

LATINA ROUNDTABLE ON HEALTH & REPRODUCTIVE RIGHTS

116 East 16th Street, 7th Fl.
New York, NY 10003

Phone: 212-533-9055
Fax: 212-982-3321
Contact: Wilma Montañez,
           Executive Director

Office Hours: 9am-5pm
Staff: Paid and volunteer
Geographic Scope: City-wide

Organizational Focus:
Advocacy and public awareness on women's health and reproductive rights issues

General Description:
Heighten community and public awareness about health problems and reproductive rights issues impacting Latinas. Advocates for needed legislative, judicial, and administrative policy reforms aimed at improving health services and reproductive options.

Bi-lingual: Spanish

Membership Organization?: No

Issues:	Constituencies:
Health Care	Latinas
HIV/AIDS	Women of
Reproductive Rights	Color
Women's Rights	

LATINO COMMISSION ON AIDS

80 Fifth Avenue
New York, NY 10011

Phone: 212-675-3288
Fax: 212-675-3466
Contact: Juan M. Mendez

Office Hours: 9:30am-5:30pm
Staff: Paid
Geographic Scope: City-wide

Organizational Focus:
Community organizing, public policy and advocacy around the AIDS crisis in the Latino community.

General Description:
The Latino Commission on AIDS is a membership organization of Latino Programs, Latinos working in AIDS, and Latinos living with HIV and AIDS. Our main advocacy areas are women with AIDS, needle exchange, harm reduction and prisoners with AIDS.

Bi-lingual: Spanish

Organizational Resources: Meeting space; workshop facilitator on public policy affecting the Latino community in AIDS crisis.

Regular Public Meetings: Quarterly membership meeting and periodic public forums

Membership Organization?: Four categories: Latino AIDS organizations; Latinos working in AIDS; Latinos living w/HIV-AIDS and Friends of the Commission

Issues:	Constituencies:
HIV/AIDS	Latino/Hispanic
	Caribbean
	Lesbian/Gay

LATINO WORKERS' CENTER

91 East 3rd Street
New York, NY

Phone: 212-473-3936
Fax: 212-473-6103
Contact: Mónica Santana, Women's
          Project Coor. & Pamela
          Galpern, Program
          Developer

Office Hours: 10am-6pm
Staff: Paid
Geographic Scope: City-wide

Organizational Focus:
Bringing together Latino workers
across industry boundaries to
support each others organizing
efforts.

General Description:
The Latino Workers' Center (also
known as the Lower East Side
Workers' Center) is a membership
organization dedicated to supporting
Latino workers' organizing efforts for
improved working conditions,
respect for their rights and a voice in
the decisions affecting their lives.

Bi-lingual: Spanish

Regular Public Meetings: Monthly
Membership Requirements:
Agreement with Center's statement
of principles/sliding-scale dues

Issues:	Constituencies:
Workers' Rights	Women
Women's Rights	Latino/Hispanic
Immigrants' Rights	
Social Justice	

LATINOS AND LATINAS DE AMBIENTE/NY (LLANY)

c/o 208 West 13th Street
New York, NY 10011

Phone: 718-588-0201
Fax: 718-673-6128
Contact: Frank J. Guzman, Co-Chair

Office: None
Geographic Scope: City-wide

Organizational Focus:
An educational, social and cultural
organization of Latino gays and
lesbians seeking to enhance our
visibility and awareness within the
Gay/Lesbian and Latino communities.

General Description:
Some of the LLANY Committees are
the Arco Iris newsletter, fundraising,
media outreach and cultural
education committee.

Bi-lingual: Spanish

Organizational Resources: Bi-
monthly Arco Iris (Rainbow) news-
letter, "Webster Hall Demonstration
Against Racism" video, "Gay-Lesbian
Race Relations" speaker.
Regular Public Meetings: Bi-monthly
at Pride Agenda Office
Membership Organization?: Yes
Membership Requirements:
Consistent attendance at meetings;
membership fees $25/yearly; support
LLANY by laws and constitution

Issues:	Constituencies:
Lesbian/Gay	Latino/Hispanic
Social Justice	Lesbian/Gay
Anti-Racism	
Arts/Culture	
HIV/AIDS	

LATINO GAY MEN OF NEW YORK

PO Box 1103
New York, NY 10025

Phone: 212-663-9148
Contact: Jose Olmo, Board Member

Office?: No
Staff: None
Geographic Scope: City-wide

Organizational Focus:
Provide a safe space for Hispanic/Latino Gay men.

General Description:
Keep members and friends informed about health, human rights/civil rights, publish and distribute 400 copies of newsletter/bulletin, cultural and social events.

Bi-lingual: Spanish

Organizational Resources: Newsletter, meeting space, and speakers.
Regular Public Meetings: 1st Friday monthly from 8-10pm at the Community Center at 208 W 13th Street.
Membership Organization?: Yes

Issues:	Constituencies:
Education	Latino/Hispanic
Anti-Violence	Multi-Racial
Anti-Racism	Gay Men
Gay Men	
HIV/AIDS	

LAWYERS ALLIANCE FOR NEW YORK

99 Hudson Street, 14th Floor
New York, NY 10013

Phone: 212-219-1800
Fax: 212-941-7458
Contact: Janet R. Faiffa, Pro-bono Program Recruitment Coordinator

Office Hours: 9:30am-5:30pm
Staff: Paid
Geographic Scope: City-wide

Organizational Focus:
Since 1969, Lawyers Alliance has been providing free and low cost corporate, real estate, and tax legal services to organizations serving low-income and disadvantaged communities.

General Description:
Through the Nonprofit Law Program, the Community Develop-ment Legal Assistance Center and the Child Care Law Program, we provide direct legal service, and coordinate the activities of pro bono volunteers.

Bi-lingual: Spanish

Organizational Resources: Newsletter; a modified hotline service wherein attorneys and non-attorneys provide answers to legal questions; a variety of legal workshops for non-profit and community development groups, and attorneys to work with these groups.
Membership Organization?: No

Issues:
Nonprofit and Child Care Law
Economic Development
Housing/Homelessness

LAWYERS COMMITTEE FOR HUMAN RIGHTS

330 Seventh Avenue, 10th Floor
New York, NY 10001

Phone: 212 629 6170
Fax: 212-967-0916
Contact: Michael Posner, Exec. Dir.

Office Hours: 9:30am-5:30pm
Staff: Paid and volunteer
Geographic Scope: City-wide

Organizational Focus:
The Lawyers Committee for Human Rights, founded in 1978, is dedicated to advancing human rights, refugee rights and the rule of law worldwide.

General Description:
The Lawyers Committee works in national and international settings to build legal systems that can enforce human rights standards and protect rights worldwide. The Committee also provides free legal representation to asylum seekers. The education and mobilization of US lawyers in human rights advocacy is an important part of our mission.

Multi-lingual: Over 15 Languages

Organizational Resources:
The LCHR publishes reports, training manuals, videos on human rights conditions and an annual report.
Membership Organization?: No

Issues:
Human Rights
Immigrants' Rights

LAWYERS' COMMITTEE ON NUCLEAR POLICY

666 Broadway, Room 625
New York, NY 10012

Phone: 212-674-7790
Fax: 212-674-6199
Contact: Alyn Ware, Executive Dir.

Office Hours: 8:30am-9:30pm
Staff: Paid and volunteer

Organizational Focus:
International law and disarmament.

General Description:
LCNP is a national non-profit educational association of lawyers, legal scholars and lay people concerned with applying national and international law to promote disarmament, in particular nuclear disarmament.

Multi-lingual: No

Organizational Resources: Newsletter and speakers.
Membership Organization?:Yes
Membership Requirements: Donation

Issues:
Peace/Anti-Militarism

LESBIAN AND GAY COMMUNITY SERVICES CENTER

208 West 13th Street
New York, NY 10011

Phone: 212-620-7310
Fax: 212-924-2657
Contact: Richard Burns, Exec. Dir.

Office Hours: 9am-11pm
Staff: Paid and volunteer
Geographic Scope: City-wide

Organizational Focus:
Lesbian and gay community - with a
focus on facilitation of community
organizing.

General Description:
Provides health, social service,
educational, recreational and cultural
programs to the lesbian and gay
community.

Organizational Resources:
Meeting space, newsletter, speakers,
workshops, health and other
program services for Lesbian and Gay
adults and youth.

Bi-lingual: Spanish

Regular Public Meetings: Yes,
throughout the year
Membership Organization?: No

Issues: Constituencies:
Lesbian/Gay   Lesbian/Gay
HIV/AIDS
Human Rights

THE LESBIAN AND GAY PEOPLE OF COLOR STEERING COMMITTEE

c/o Lidell Jackson
210 Riverside Drive, Suite 11-H
New York, NY 10025

Phone: 212-222-9794
Contact: Lidell Jackson, Secretary

Office: No
Staff: None
Geographic Scope: City-wide

General Description:
The LGPOCSC is a NYC-based
coalition of over 30 lesbian and gay
People of Color organizations. Its
mission is to collectively pool the
resources of each individual group
represented on issues of mutual
concern while working to increase
the visibility, voice, and presence of
People of Color in the lesbian and
gay community, in their respective
communities, and in the political
arena.

Regular Public Meetings: Every 1st
Tuesday or Wednesday (alternating)
at the Lesbian and Gay Community
Services Center, 208 W. 13th Street.
Membership Organization?: No

Issues: Constituencies:
Lesbian/Gay   Multi-Racial
Int'l Solidarity   Lesbian/Gay
Anti-Racism

THE LESBIAN AVENGERS

c/o The Center
208 West 13th Street
New York, NY 10011

Phone: 212- 967-7711 ext. 3204
Contact: Marlene Colburn

Office Hours: 24hr hotline; no office
Staff: Volunteer
Geographic Scope: City-wide and national

Organizational Focus:
The Lesbian Avengers is a direct action group using grassroots activism and direct action to fight for the survival and visibility of all Lesbians.

General Description:
Our purpose is to identify and promote issues and perspectives from various lesbian communities while empowering lesbians to become experienced organizers who can participate in political rebellion.

Regular Public Meetings?: Tuesdays 8pm at Center

Issues:	Constituencies:
Anti-Racism	Lesbian
Lesbian	
Social Justice	

THE LIVING THEATRE, INC.

800 West End Avenue, #5A
New York, NY 10025

Phone: 212- 865-3957
Fax: 212-865-3234
Contact: Joanie Fritz, Managing Dir.

Office Hours: 10am-5pm
Staff: Paid and volunteer
Geographic Scope: City-wide, mainly Lower East Side

Organizational Focus:
Revolutionary theatre

General Description:
The Living Theatre, co-founded by Judith Malina and the late Julian Beck in 1947, continues to investigate the sociopolitical relationship between actor and public, with theatre addressing the challenging questions of our times.

Multi-lingual: Spanish, Italian, German and French

Organizational Resources: Annual newsletter, Living Theatre Archives-NYC Public Library, films/videos, workshop facilitators-Living Theatre techniques, Not in My Name: Anti-Death Penalty Play, and hotline 212-969-8905.
Regular Public Meetings?: Open rehearsals

Issues:	Constituencies:
Arts/Culture	Multi-Racial
Peace/	BNVAR
Anti-Militarism	
Anti-Racism	

LOWER EAST SIDE ANTI-DISPLACEMENT PROJECT, INC.

638 East 6th Street, 2nd Floor
New York, NY 10009

Phone: 212-629-9720
Fax: 212-677-7166
Contact: A. Averette, Exec. Dir. or
D. Wilson, Housing
Advocate

Office Hours: Mon.-Thurs. 10am-
2pm walk-in service
Staff: Volunteer
Geographic Scope: City-wide

Organizational Focus:
Tenants' rights and entitlement advocacy ranging from Jiggetts V. Glass Preliminary Relief to food stamps.

General Description:
Not for profit housing rights organization.

Organizational Resources: Pamphlets and meeting space.
Regular Public Meetings: May and October
Membership Organization?: No

Issues: Constituencies:
Housing/   Latino/Hispanic
Homelessness   Multi-Racial
Legal   Disabled people
Housing Advocacy   Lesbian/Gay
Welfare Advocacy

LOWER EAST SIDE CALL FOR JUSTICE

c/o Abe Markman
675 Water Street, Apt. 5-C
New York, NY 10002

Phone: 212-964-9681
Contact: Abe Markman, Co-Chair

Office: No
Staff: None
Geographic Scope: Lower East Side

Organizational Focus:
Empower Lower East Side residents to deal effectively with police misuse of power.

General Description:
The Lower East Side Call for Justice has been very active in promoting and supporting the Civilian Complaint Review Board; holding educational forums; and recently publishing a manual for teenagers, *Do's and Don't s When Arrested.*

Organizational Resources: The manual is available for youth groups willing to hold a workshop to explain it to teenagers. Write or call Abe Markman for more information.
Membership Organization?: Yes
Membership Requirements:
Interested in promoting our goals

Issues:
Social Justice

LOWER EAST SIDE HARM REDUCTION CENTER

223 East 2nd Street
New York, NY 10009

Phone: 212-477-6863
Fax: 212-477-7015
Contact: Allan Clear, Exec. Director

Office?: Yes
Staff: Paid and volunteer
Geographic Scope: Lower East Side

Organizational Focus:
Providing clean needles, health education and other harm reduction resources to identified drug users with the goal of HIV prevention.

General Description:
To prevent the spread of HIV among drug injectors. We also provide drug user support, targeted intervention and support groups.

Multi-lingual: Spanish and French

Organizational Resources:
Newsletter, pamphlets and other literature about harm reduction and needle exchange in addition to our outreach program.
Membership Organization?: No

Issues: Constituencies:
HIV/AIDS   Drug users
Human Rights
Social Justice

LOWER EAST SIDE JOINT PLANNING COUNCIL

61 East 4th Street
New York, NY 10003

Phone: 212-473-2837
Fax: 212-477-9328
Contact: Benjamin Dulchin, Exec.
          Director

Office Hours: Mon.-Fri. 10am-6pm
Staff: Paid and volunteer
Geographic Scope: Lower East Side

Organizational Focus:
Affordable housing and neighbor-hood preservation.

General Description:
The Lower East Side Joint Planning Council works to preserve the neighborhood as a multi-ethnic, economically-diverse community by organizing to protect and increase the supply of affordable housing and by maintaining a strong community coalition.

Multi-lingual: Spanish, Mandarin, Cantonese

Membership Organization?: No

Issues: Constituencies:
Housing   Multi-Racial
Economic Development

LOWER MANHATTAN LOFT TENANTS

PO Box 20239, Greeley Sq. Station
New York, NY 10001

Phone: 212-683-5507
Fax: Same/Call first
Contact: Ray Bailey, Co-Chair

Office Hours: Mon.-Fri. 9am-5pm
Staff: Paid and volunteer
Geographic Scope: City-wide

Organizational Focus:
Advocacy organization for residential
loft tenants in NYC.

General Description:
Lower Manhattan Loft Tenants
lobbies elected officials and
administrators, monitors
administrative agencies, brings legal
challenges when necessary,
formulates solid, defensible positions
for regulation changes and strategy
interpretations, counsels members
and keeps them informed.

Bi-lingual: Spanish

Organizational Resources:
Newsletter
Regular Public Meetings: Tuesdays 5-
7pm., 280 Broadway, Rm. 412
Membership Organization?:Yes
Membership Requirements: Must
live in loft and pay membership dues.

Issues: Constituencies:
Housing   Residential Loft
                   Tenants

MADRE

121 West 27th Street
New York, NY 10001

Phone: 212-627-0444
Fax: 212-675-0444
Contact: Vivian Stromberg, Ex. Dir.

Office Hours: 9:30am- 5:30pm
Staff: Paid
Geographic Scope: NYC and
National

Organizational Focus:
Women's Human Rights

General Description:
MADRE is a 20,000 member, multi-
racial, cross-class, national women's
organization. Our goal is to further
the possibilities of peace and justice
through a women's human rights
agenda internationally and in the US.

Bi-lingual: Spanish

Organizational Resources: MADRE
has a speakers' bureau as well as a
women's documentation center.
MADRE also provides pamphlets,
videos, newsletters and brochures
Membership Organization?: Yes, $25
fee

Issues: Constituencies:
Women's Rights   Multi-Racial
Children
Human Rights

MANHATTAN VALLEY DEVELOPMENT CORPORATION (MVDC)

73 West 108th Street
New York, NY 10025

Phone: 212-749-4410
Fax: 212-749-4466
Contact: Leah Schneider, Exec. Dir.

Office Hours: Mon.-Fri. 9am-5pm
Staff: Paid
Geographic Scope: Manhattan Valley

Organizational Focus:
Production of safe, affordable housing
and stabilization of Manhattan Valley
community.

General Description:
MVDC, a not-for-profit community-
based organization, established in
1968, serves the Manhattan Valley
neighborhood of predominantly low
income minority residents. MVDC's
projects include permanent housing
for homeless/doubled-up families and
individuals.

Bi-lingual: Spanish

Organizational Resources:
Newsletter (occasionally)
Membership Organization?:Yes
Membership Requirement: Interest
in the community revitalization

Issues:	Constituencies
Housing/	Multi-Racial
Homelessness	

MASS TRANSIT STREET THEATER

PO Box 347
Bronx, NY 10468

Phone: 718-937-8277
Contact: Ellen M. Pollan, Adm. Dir.

Office Hours: Part-time, flexible.
Staff: Paid
Geographic Scope: City-wide

Organizational Focus:
To provide professional quality
theatrical performances which reflect
and celebrate the efforts people
make to improve their lives. To use
our original theater to initiate
dialogue and organize communities.

General Description:
Mass Transit addresses the real
condition of people's lives, depicting
characters from the same economic
and social backgrounds as the
audience. We encourage our
audiences to focus on their strengths
and abilities while examining
personal, social, and political issues.

Organizational Resources:
Workshops, facilitators
Membership Organization?: No

Issues:	Constituencies:
Arts/Culture	Multi-Racial
Women	
Youth	

MEDIA ALLIANCE

c/o WNET
356 West 58th Street
New York, NY 10019

Phone: 212-560-2919
Fax: 212-560-6866
Contact: Mona Jimenez, Exec. Dir.

Office Hours: Mon.-Fri. 10am-5pm
Staff: Paid
Geographic Scope: Statewide

Organizational Focus:
Media Alliance is a non profit
membership organization of media
organizations and independent
producers.

General Description:
Media Alliance provides information
on media resources, and advocates
for funding and public policy to
ensure that independent media
producers have equipment, training
and access to distribution.

Organizational Resources:
Newsletter, annual conference,
workshops, contacts,
Regular Public Meetings: Yes
Membership Organization?: Yes
Membership Requirements: $20-
$30/person; $100-150/organizations.

Issues:	Constituencies:
Media	Media Makers
Arts/Culture	Media Orgs.

MEDIA NETWORK

39 West 14th Street, Suite 403
New York, NY 10011

Phone: 212 929-2663
Contact: Ilana Navaro, Membership
          & Outreach Coordinator

Office Hours: 10am-6pm
Staff: Paid
Geographic Scope: National

Organizational Focus:
To promote the production and use
of independent social issue media.

General Description:
The fiscal sponsorship program
provides independent video and
filmmakers with tax exempt status
and creative advice on proposal
development and fundraising. The
media literacy program teaches
people how to use media to talk
about and fight AIDS, racism, sexism,
and homophobia.

Bi-lingual: Spanish

Organizational Resources:
Workshops, guides, newsletters,
speakers & facilities.
Regular Public Meetings: Yes
Membership Organization?: Yes
Membership Requirements: $35/
person $50/organization.

Issues:	Constituencies:
Media	All interested in
AIDS	media
Racism	Multi-Racial
Sexism	
Homophobia	

MEGA-CITIES: NEW YORK

915 Broadway, Suite 1601
New York, NY 10010

Phone: 212-979-7644
Fax: 212-979-7624
Contact: NYC Director

Office Hours: Mon.-Fri. 9am-5pm
Staff: Paid
Geographic Scope: City-wide

Organizational Focus:
To find, promote, and transfer innovative solutions to urban problems; to impact public policy.

General Description:
We seek innovative solutions to urban problems, assist in replicating these in new settings (local and global) and work with outstanding community leaders to maximize their effectiveness. The New York City offices is one of 20 field sites in the Mega-Cities global network.

Organizational Resources:
Periodic conferences and workshops. Call to be placed on mailing list if you would like to receive ongoing information.
Regular Public Meetings: Yes
Membership Organization?: No

Issues: Constituencies:
Urban Issues   Urban Dwellers
Social Justice
Econ. Development
Environment

MET COUNCIL ON HOUSING

102 Fulton Street, Rm. 302
New York, NY 10038

Phone: 212-693-0550
Contact: Jenny Laurie, Director

Office Hours: Mon.-Wed. & Friday
                1:30-5pm
Staff: Paid and volunteer
Geographic Scope: Manhattan, Brooklyn and Queens

General Description:
Met Council is a city-wide tenants' union. We advocate for tenants' rights and help tenants enforce their rights through organizing and counseling.

Bi-lingual: Spanish

Organizational Resources:
Newsletter, newspaper, *Tenant/Inquilino*, tenants' rights pamphlets.
Membership Organization?: Yes
Membership Requirements: $18/yr membership fee

Issues: Constituencies:
Tenants' Rights   Tenants
Housing/Homeless
Gov't Accountability

METROPOLITAN NEW YORK PEACE ACTION COUNCIL

475 Riverside Drive
New York, NY 10115

Phone: 212-870-2304
Fax: 212-870-2243
Contact: Ken Estey, Exec. Director

Office Hours: 9am-4pm
Staff: Paid
Geographic Scope: City-wide

Organizational Focus:
The mission of Metropolitan New York Peace Action Council is to educate and motivate people to strive for disarmament, economic conversion, the end to weapons trafficking, a clean environment and for peaceful resolution to conflict.

General Description: We achieve this through educational programs, direct action (peaceful rallies and demonstrations) and town and chapter meetings.

Organizational Resources:
Newsletter, literature on peace and disarmament issues.
Membership Organization?: Yes
Membership Requirements: $25 Donation

Issues:	Constituencies:
Peace/	Multi-Racial
Anti-Militarism	
Disarmament	
Anti-Violence	
Environment	

MFY LEGAL SERVICES, INC.

41 Avenue A
New York, NY 10009

Phone: 212-475-8000
Fax: 212-475-1043
Contact: Wayne G. Hawley, Exec. Director

Office Hours: 9:30am-5:30pm
Staff: Paid
Geographic Scope: East Side of Manhattan and Westside from West 34th-110th.

Organizational Focus:
Ensuring that poor New Yorkers are not denied equal access to justice because they cannot afford a lawyer.

General Description:
MFY provides high quality legal services and supportive social work services in civil matters to low income individuals, families, and groups in the NYC communities it serves. MFY protects its clients' rights by enforcing existing laws, advocating for necessary change in laws, and educating the community.

Multi-lingual: Spanish & Chinese

Organizational Resources:
Brochures
Membership Organization?: No

Issues:	Constituencies:
Legal	Low Income
Housing/	residents of
Homelessness	Manhattan
Welfare Advocacy	

MOTHERS AGAINST VIOLENCE, BRONX CHAPTER

800 Concourse Village, Suite 151
Bronx, NY 10456

Phone: 718-617-6020
Fax: 718-617-6020
Contact: Lynn Anderson Carter,
          Director

Office?: Yes
Staff: Volunteer
Geographic Scope: Bronx

Organizational Focus:
Mobilize youth and the community to take action to prevent violence and understand the causes.

General Description:
We focus on youth against youth violence by promoting forums for dialogue, a safe house for positive socialization, and activities to begin the healing process of the communities ravaged by violence.

Bi-lingual: Spanish

Organizational Resources:
Pamphlets, speakers, newsletter
Regular Public Meetings: Every 3rd Friday at Bronx Lebanon.
Membership Organization?: Yes
Membership Requirements:
Commitment to stop violence.

Issues: Constituencies:
Anti-Violence   Youth
Youth   Women
Education   Multi-Racial
Human Rights   Young Men
Anti-Racism

NATIONAL ABORTION & REPRODUCTIVE RIGHTS ACTION LEAGUE

462 Broadway, Rm. 540
New York, NY 10013

Phone: 212-343-0114
Fax: 212-343-0119
Contact: Annie Keating, Program
          Director

Office Hours: Mon.-Fri. 10am-6pm
Staff: Paid
Geographic Scope: Statewide

Organizational Focus:
To protect and expand women's reproductive rights including access to safe, legal abortions.

General Description:
NARAL/NY's membership, foundation and political action branches enable us to do legislative and electoral work, education, organizing and advocacy. We run a youth training initiative and a media project. We also participate in issue coalitions.

Organizational Resources:
Pamphlets on minors' access to abortion, a source book that lists abortion providers throughout the state, a prochoice guide to corporate giving, voting guides for elections and updated organizing materials.
Regular Public Meetings: Monthly, for all interested new volunteers/ activists.
Membership Organization?: Yes
Membership Requirements: $25 year sliding scale

Issues:
Reproductive Rights

NATIONAL COALITION FOR HAITIAN REFUGEES

275 7th Avenue, 25th Floor.
New York, NY 10001

Phone: 212-337-0005
Fax: 212-337-0028
Contact: Jocelyn McCalla, Exec. Dir.

Office?:   Yes
Staff: Paid
Geographic Scope: City-wide

Organizational Focus:
Promoting human rights and justice.

General Description:
The National Coalition for Haitian
Refugees, an alliance of some of the
leading US civil rights, labor, religious
and immigrants' rights organizations,
is dedicated to securing justice for
Haitian asylum-seekers and
promoting both human rights in Haiti
and empowerment of Haitians
residing in the United States.

Multi-lingual: Haitian Creole, French,

Organizational Resources:
Newsletter, reports, publications,
speakers, seminars and conferences.
Membership Organization?: Yes

Issues: Constituencies:
Human Rights   Haitian
Immigrants' Rights
Social Justice
Econ. Development (Haiti)

NATIONAL CONGRESS FOR PUERTO RICAN RIGHTS/NYC CHAPTER

PO Box 205-098, Sunset Sta.
Brooklyn, NY 11220

Phone: 718-388-8056
Fax: 718-788-4986
Contact: Annette Hernandez, Chair

Office?:   No
Staff: Volunteer
Geographic Scope: City-wide

General Description:
Since 1981, the National Congress
for Puerto Rican Rights has worked
for community empowerment.
Activities include advocacy,
educational forums and support of
shared political awareness among
Latinos and the Puerto Rican
community, in particular.

Bi-lingual: Spanish

Organizational Resources: News-
letter, *Latino Issues Update*, and
speakers
Regular Public Meetings: May &
October Forums
Membership Organization?: Yes
Membership Requirements: $15/yr

Issues: Constituencies:
Anti-Racism   Latino/Hispanic
Social Justice   Youth
Youth   Multi-Racial
Environment

NATIONAL LABOR COMMITTEE IN SUPPORT OF WORKER & HUMAN RIGHTS IN CENTRAL AMERICA

15 Union Square
New York, NY 10003

Phone: 212-242-0700
Fax: 212-255-7230
Contact: Ralph Rivera, Assoc. Dir.
Staff: Paid
Geographic Scope: National

Organizational Focus:
Our primary purpose is to defend and promote human and workers' rights internationally and to develop specially targeted campaigns that seek to educate the American public about how substandard working conditions abroad directly impact on living standards in the U.S.

General Description:
1) Conducts innovative research linking internationally recognized worker rights with free trade policy and foreign assistance programs; 2) Sponsors U.S public education campaigns 3) Organizes emergency support networks.

Bi-lingual: Spanish

Organizational Resources: Special Reports: "Paying to Lose our Jobs," "Haiti after the Coup," "Free Trades Hidden Secrets" and others.
Membership Organization?: No

Issues:
Workers' Rights
Human Rights
Int'l Solidarity

NATIONAL LAWYERS GUILD (NLG)

55 Avenue of the Americas
New York, NY 10013

Phone: 212-966-5000
Fax: 212-966-9714
Contact: Martin Sanchez, Exec. Dir.

Office Hours: 10am-5pm
Staff: Paid and volunteer
Geographic Scope: City-wide and national

Organizational Focus:
The National Lawyers Guild is a progressive legal organization working for social justice.

General Description:
The NLG is a national network of over 6,000 social-change oriented members: lawyers, legal workers, law students and jailhouse lawyers who look upon the law as an instrument for the protection of the people, rather than for their repression.

Bi-lingual: Spanish

Organizational Resources: Newsletter, various manuals including law student organizing, an AIDS manual, and an immigration manual.
Regular Public Meetings: Yes, an annual convention & many more
Membership Organization?: Yes
Membership Requirements: Dues

Issues:	Constituencies:
Legal	Multi-Racial
Social Justice	Women
Human Rights	
Immigrants' Rights	
HIV/AIDS	

NATIONAL ORGANIZATION FOR WOMEN (NOW-NYC)

22 West 21st Street, Suite 701
New York, NY 10010

Phone: 212-807-0721
Fax: 212-727-1961
Contact: Diane H. Welsh, President

Office Hours: 10am-10pm
Staff: Paid and volunteer
Geographic Scope: City-wide and a chapter of a national organization

Organizational Focus:
Women's Rights and within that our priority issues are abortion and reproductive rights, ending racism, passing an ERA, ending violence against women, and lesbian rights.

General Description:
Oldest, and largest feminist organization. Founded in 1966-67, NOW-NYC is the founding chapter. We are a grassroots action organization that is multi-issue and multi-strategy.

Organizational Resources:
Newsletter, pamphlets, meeting space, speakers' bureau, and workshop facilitators.
Regular Public Meetings: 1st Tuesday of every month 5:30-7pm.
Membership Organization?: Yes
Membership Requirements: Belief in NOW's purposes.

Issues: Constituencies:
Women's Rights   Women

NATIONAL WOMEN'S POLITICAL CAUCUS

271 West 125th Street, Suite 211
New York, NY 10027

Phone: 212-961-1000
Fax: 212-961-1015
Contact: Peggy Shepard, VP NYS & Pres. Manhattan Chapter

Staff: Volunteer
Geographic Scope: Statewide with chapters in each county.

Organizational Focus:
Electing and appointing feminist women to office and training women to run for office and work in campaigns.

General Description:
The NWPC is a grassroots, activist women's organization committed to supporting and raising funds for feminist candidates, mobilizing women to work in campaigns and training women to take leadership in campaigns and/or to run for office.

Organizational Resources: Newsletter, speakers' bureau, campaign handbook and other how-to manuals on starting chapters, fundraising, etc,
Regular Public Meetings: Yes
Membership Organization?: Yes
Membership Requirements: Open to pro-choice women of any political party. Annual dues.

Issues: Constituencies
Women's Rights   Multi-Racial
Child care
Domestic Violence
Lesbian/Gay

NEIGHBORHOOD OPEN SPACE COALITION

72 Reade Street
New York, NY 10007

Phone: 212-513-7555
Fax: 212-385-6095
Contact: Anne McClellan, Exec. Dir.

Office Hours: Mon-Fri. 8am-7pm
Staff: Paid and volunteer

Organizational Focus:
Enhancing the quality of life for all
New Yorkers by expanding and
protecting our City's parks and open
spaces.

General Description:
Created in 1980, we are now a
working partnership of over125
organizations. Coalition members
engage in advocacy, research and
planning to ensure that parks and
open spaces are a high priority in
City planning, programs and policies.

Organizational Resources:
Newsletter, annual budget analysis,
position papers on a wide variety of
planning and physical development
projects, and a reference library.
Membership Organization?: Yes
Membership Requirements: Dues

Issues:
Environment

NEIGHBORS TOGETHER

160 Thomas Boyland Street
Brooklyn, NY 11218

Phone: 718-498-7256
Fax: 718-498-7159 call first
Contact: Anne Kohler, Exec. Dir.

Office Hours: Mon.-Fri. 9am-4pm
Staff: Paid and volunteer
Geographic Scope: Brownsville,
Bushwick, East NY

Organizational Focus:
To address the immediate problem
and underlying causes of hunger.

General Description:
We provide daily meals to an average
of 500 Brownsville, Bedford, East
New York and Bushwick, Brooklyn
residents. Neighbors Together
engages in system-wide efforts to
change and influence regulations
affecting the population; provides
counseling and social services to
empower clients; and is committed
to the elimination of hunger.

Organizational Resources:
Newsletter, meeting space, and meals
served from 11am - 2pm.
Membership Organization?: No

Issues:	Constituencies:
Social Justice	African American
Human Rights	
Welfare Advocacy	

NETWORK OF BLACK ORGANIZERS (NOBO)

402 West 145 Street
New York, NY 10031

Phone: 212-928-5896
Contact: Sam Anderson, Co-
           Founder/Senior Ed

Office Hours: 8:30am-6pm
Staff: Volunteer
Geographic Scope: City-wide

Organizational Focus:
Rebuilding (helping) the Black
liberation movement through
networking, study and organizing.

General Description:
We produce a quarterly journal:
NOBO, forming the Ella Baker
Center for African American Praxis,
and we hold NOBO poetry jams that
promote progressive Black culture.

Bi-lingual: Spanish

Organizational Resources:
Newsletter, journal (Nobo), books,
pamphlets, posters, school for
organizers, Black poetry & music
outlet.
Regular Public Meetings: Yes
Membership Organization?: Yes
Membership Requirements: African
descent

Issues:	Constituencies:
Anti-Racism	African American
Human Rights	Latino/Hispanic
Social Justice	Multi-Racial
Education	
Arts/Culture	

NEW FEDERAL THEATER

466 Grand Street
New York, NY 10002

Phone: 212-589-0400
Fax: 212-505-8329
Contact: Woodie King, Jr.,
           Producing Director

Office Hours: 10am-6pm
Staff: Paid
Geographic Scope: City-wide

Organizational Focus:
New Federal Theatre's focus is on
producing theatre that reaches out
to a minority audience.

General Description:
The organization is multi-cultural. Its
actor training workshops are for
teens, adults and playwrights.

Multi-lingual: No

Organizational Resources: Speakers'
bureau, workshops in playwriting and
workshops in acting.
Membership Organization?:No

Issues:	Constituencies:
Arts/Culture	African American
Youth	Latino/Hispanic
Students	Multi-Racial
	Women

NEW YORK AIDS COALITION

231 West 29 Street
New York, NY 10001

Phone: 212 629-3075
Fax: 212-629-8403
Contact: Amy Herman, Exec. Dir.

Office Hours: Mon.-Fri. 9am-5pm
Staff: Paid
Geographic Scope: City-wide

Organizational Focus:
HIV/AIDS advocacy and education

General Description:
NYAC was established in 1988 to
enable all communities affected by
HIV/AIDS to advocate with one voice
for increased funding and fair policies
on the state and local level.

Organizational Resources: Newsletter, written material, resource
information, policy alerts, & trainings.
Membership Organization?: Yes

Issues:
HIV/AIDS

NEW YORK ASIAN WOMEN'S CENTER

39 Bowery, #375
New York, NY 10002

Phone: 212-732-5230
Contact: Patricia Eng, Exec. Dir.

Office Hours: Mon.-Fri. 9am-5pm
Staff: Paid
Geographic Scope: City-wide

Organizational Focus:
Domestic violence, violence against
women in Asian communities.

General Description:
We provide counseling, legal
assistance, and run a shelter. We
also act as advocates and organize
around domestic violence issues.
We participate in coalitions and
sponsor events.

Multi-lingual: Chinese, Korean, &
other Asian languages.

Organizational Resources:
Newsletter, pamphlets, hotline, and
speakers' bureau.
Membership Organization?: No

Issues: Constituencies:
Domestic Violence   Asian/Pacific
Women's Rights   Islander
Anti-Violence

NEW YORK BLACK WOMEN'S HEALTH PROJECT

PO Box 401037
Brooklyn, NY 11240

Phone: 212-439-8749
Contact: Gwendolyn Braxton,
           Member
Office?:   No
Staff: Volunteer
Geographic Scope: City-wide

Organizational Focus:
Currently, we are focusing on the training of trainers (peer) to lead self-help groups, provide health education, and advocate for health and well-being.

General Description:
NYBWHP promotes health and well-being through self help groups; health education workshops, conferences, literature, health advocacy for Black women, families, communities and allies in NYC.

Organizational Resources:
Literature, speakers, workshops & workshop facilitators
Regular Public Meetings: Yes
Membership Organization?: Yes
Membership Requirements: Active participation and pay annual dues.

Issues:	Constituencies:
Health/Well-being	African American
Health Care	Caribbean
Anti-Violence	Women
Anti-Racism	Youth
Human Rights	

NEW YORK CITY COALITION AGAINST HUNGER

11 John Street, Room 703
New York, NY 10038

Phone: 212-227-8480
Fax: 212-385-4300
Contact: Judith Walker, Exec. Dir.

Office Hours: Mon.-Thur., 9am-6pm
Staff: Paid and volunteer
Geographic Scope: City-wide

Organizational Focus:
Public education, policy development and advocacy to help NYC's grassroots network of emergency feeding programs relieve hunger immediately. In the long term, it seeks to eliminate hunger and the need for emergency food programs.

General Description:
The only citywide membership organization for soup kitchens, food pantries and anti-hunger organizations to provide a collective voice in the fight to end hunger.

Organizational Resources:
Pamphlets which document statistics on hunger and other problems arising from hunger. We also hold workshops and interfaith services against hunger.
Regular Public Meetings: 2nd Wednesday of the month
Membership Organization?: Yes
Membership Requirements:
Commitment to ending hunger

Issues:	Constituencies:
Hunger Advocacy	Hungry People
Welfare Advocacy	Homeless People
Housing/Homelessness	

NEW YORK CITY ENVIRONMENTAL JUSTICE ALLIANCE

271 West 125 Street, Room 303
New York, NY 10027

Phone: 212-866-4120
Fax: 212-866-4511
Contact: Michelle DePass, Exec. Dir

Office Hours: 9am-5pm
Staff: Paid and volunteer
Geographic Scope: City-wide

Organizational Focus:
Ensuring an environment that
sustains health, equal environmental
protection and open participation in
determining environmental policy.

General Description:
The Alliance links grassroots
organizations concerned with
ensuring the right of communities of
color and low income communities
to a clean and safe environment.
NYCEJA educates and advocates,
facilitates a city-wide network,
sponsors events and forums and acts
as an information clearinghouse.

Bi-lingual: Spanish

Organizational Resources: News-
letter, speakers' bureaus, pamphlets,
technical and legal resources.
Regular Public Meetings: Every other
month
Membership Organization?: Yes
Membership Requirements:
Commitment to our goals

Issues:	Constituencies:
Environment	All people of
Social Justice	color
Transportation	Low Income
	communities

NEW YORK CITY LABOR AND ENVIRONMENT NETWORK

150 West 28th Street, Ste. 1501
New York, NY 10001

Phone: 212-714-8005
Fax: 212-645-2214
Contact: Jeff Vogel, Coordinating
          Committee Member

Office Hours: Variable
Staff: None
Geographic Scope: City-wide

Organizational Focus:
NYCLEN'S aim is to build bridges
between labor advocates and
environmentalists to forge a common
strategy for economic and
environmental sustainability.

General Description:
NYCLEN holds monthly educational
forums on issues ranging from
economic development, GATT and
NAFTA to urban toxics. The
network tracks state and local
legislation, produces a newsletter and
organizes a regional conference.

Organizational Resources:
Library and bibliography, hotline,
newsletter with calendar
Regular Public Meetings: Yes
Membership Organization?: Yes
Membership Requirements:
Commitment to goals

Issues:	Constituencies:
Environment	Union Members
Labor	Multi-Racial
Econ. Development	

NEW YORK CITY/LESBIAN HEALTH FAIR (NYC/LHF)

c/o Community Health Project
208 West 13th Street, 2nd Floor
New York, NY 10011

Phone: 212-675-3559
Office: None
Staff: None
Geographic Scope: City-wide

General Description:
The annual Lesbian Health Fair offers lesbians throughout the NYC metropolitan area access to free health services and health information in order to empower lesbians of all ages in seeking and making vital health care choices.

Multi-lingual: Fair offers ASL, Cantonese, Spanish and Kreyol translations. Journal is in Spanish and English.

Organizational Resources: The NYC/LHF Journal.
Membership Organization?: No

Issues: Constituencies:
Health Care   Lesbian
Lesbian   Multi-Racial
Youth

NEW YORK CITY STREETSINGERS

c/o George Robinson
32 East 35th Street
New York, NY 10016

Phone: 212-475-3049
Contact: George Robinson, Exec. Officer
Office: No
Staff: None
Geographic Scope: City-wide

Organizational Focus:
Music: singing as a way to demonstrate how NY's varied communities can make harmony.

General Description:
We seek members from all of NY's many communities. We attend mostly public events. We accept invitations to sing at demonstrations of public conscience.

Multi-lingual: Spanish, Asian, and African songs

Organizational Resources:
We have occasionally organized a coalition of choruses.
Regular Public Meetings: Every Tuesday 6pm at Community Church of New York
Membership Organization?: No

Issues:
City-wide Solidarity
Anti-Racism
Anti-Violence

NEW YORK CIVIL LIBERTIES UNION

132 West 43rd Street
New York, NY 10036

Phone: 212-382-0557
Fax: 212-354-2583
Contact: Sandra Zickefoose,
          Development Dir.

Office Hours: Mon.-Fri., 9:30-5:30pm
Staff: Paid
Geographic Scope: City-wide and statewide

Organizational Focus:
Through a three-tiered strategy of litigation, advocacy and public education the NYCLU strives to ensure that the civil rights and civil liberties guaranteed to all in the NY and US constitutions are not infringed. Call today to volunteer.

Bi-lingual: Spanish (but not for intake)

Organizational Resources:
Newsletter, reproductive rights workshops, fact sheets, policy statements, speakers' bureau.
Regular Public Meetings?: General membership mtg. in February
Membership Organization?:, $20 general membership fee, low-income fee $5.00

Issues:
Civil Liberties
Legal
Social Justice
Human Rights

NEW YORK CLINIC DEFENSE TASK FORCE (NYCDTF)

PO Box 2374
New York, NY 10009

Phone: 212-967-7711 ext.: 3564
Contact: Elieen Gordon

Office: No
Staff: Volunteer
Geographic Scope: City-wide

Organizational Focus:
Clinic defense and access to women's health facilities.

General Description:
Originally a coalition of groups including WHAM!, NOW, NARAL, Planned Parenthood and the Fund for the Feminist Majority, NYCDTF is now an independent group dedicated to peaceably countering the harassment and violence of Operation Rescue and similar anti-choice terrorist groups at women's health care facilities. NYCDTF has trained thousands of New Yorkers in nonviolent clinic defense tactics.

Organizational Resources: Hotline, escort trainings, clinic defense trainings, community/political outreach.

Issues: Constituencies:
Clinic Defense   Women
Women's Health Care
Reproductive Rights
Women's Rights

NEW YORK COMMITTEE IN SOLIDARITY WITH THE PEOPLE OF EL SALVADOR

19 West 21 Street, #502
New York, NY 10010

Phone: 212-645-5230
Fax: 212-645-7280
Contact: Greg Wilpert, Coordinator

Staff: Paid
Geographic Scope: City-wide

Organizational Focus:
El Salvador Solidarity

General Description:
Work against US efforts to dominate
Latin America: actively helping to
build an alternative with participatory
democracy, human rights, economic
justice. CISPES works to challenge
racism, sexism, homophobia, and
other forms of oppression.

Bi-lingual: Spanish

Organizational Resources:
Newsletter
Regular Public Meetings: Yes
Membership Organization?: No

Issues:
Social Justice
Int'l Solidarity
Anti-Racism
Workers' Rights
Women's Rights

NEW YORK DEMOCRATIC SOCIALISTS OF AMERICA

180 Varick Street, 12th Floor
New York, NY 10014

Phone: 212-727-2207
Fax: 212-727-8616
Contact: Sheila Johnson, Organizer

Office Hours: Vary
Staff: Paid
Geographic Scope: City-wide

Organizational Focus:
DSA advocates for a democratic
socialist society through educational
and activist work.

General Description:
We believe economic security is a
human right and place human needs
above the needs of the market. We
fight to end racism, sexism and
homophobia by building multiracial
coalitions rooted in a shared vision of
social and economic justice.

Organizational Resources:
Newsletter and meeting program.
Regular Public Meetings: Yes,
advertised in the newsletter
Membership Organization?: Yes
Membership Requirements: $35 dues,
$20 for students, or low income.

Issues:
Social Justice
Anti-Racism
Int'l Solidarity
Lesbian/Gay

NEW YORK GRAY PANTHERS

15 West 65 Street, Rm. 519
New York, NY 10023

Phone: 212-799-7572
Contact: Edna Graig

Office Hours: Tues. & Thurs.
11:30am-3pm
Staff: Volunteer
Geographic Scope: City-wide

Organizational Focus:
Advocates for social justice

General Description:
The Gray Panthers is an organization
of seniors who mobilize ourselves
and others for social justice. Each
year we adopt an organizing priority.
1994's was health care.

Organizational Resources:
Newsletter
Regular Public Meetings: Monthly
Sept. through June.
Membership Organization?: Yes

Issues:	Constituencies:
Senior	Seniors
Social Justice	
Health Care	

NEW YORK PUBLIC INTEREST RESEARCH GROUP (NYPIRG)

9 Murray Street, 3rd Floor
New York, NY 10007

Phone: 212-349-6460
Fax: 212-349-1366
Contact: Ludovic Blain, Environ-
mental Justice Advocate

Office Hours: 9am-6pm
Staff: Paid
Geographic Scope: City-wide

Organizational Focus:
Environmental and consumer
protection, government and
corporate accountability, economic
and social justice.

General Description:
NYPIRG is a not-for-profit,
nonpartisan research advocacy and
organizing organization. NYPIRG's
staff and students work to shape
public policy and develop citizen
participation in the areas of its
organizational focus.

Organizational Resources: Newsletter, environmental information,
higher education funding facts, and
speakers on a wide variety of issues.
Membership Organization?: Yes
Membership Requirements: Annual
contribution

Issues:	Constituencies:
Gov't Accountability	Multi-Racial
Environment	Students
Voting Rights	Youth
Social Justice	

NEW YORK STATE COMMON CAUSE

150 Nassau Street, Suite 1823
New York, NY 10038

Phone: 212-349-1755
Fax: 212-349-8724
Contact: Andrew Greenblatt, Exec.
          Director

Office Hours: 9am-6pm
Staff: Paid
Geographic Scope: City-wide

Organizational Focus:
Clean-up campaigns and control
campaign spending; end incumbent
abuses; ease access to the ballot for
voters and candidates.

General Description:
Non-profit, nonpartisan, good
government, citizens' lobby group.
Our mission is to lessen the amount
of influence that special interests
have on our government and to
make our representatives more
accountable and responsive to the
people that they represent.

Organizational Resources: Pamphlets,
reports, newsletter, and a speakers'
bureau.
Regular Public Meetings: Monthly
Membership Organization?:Yes
Membership Requirements: $20
donation

Issues:	Constituencies:
Gov't Accountability	Multi-Racial
Voting Rights	
Social Justice	
Civil Rights	

NEW YORK STATEWIDE SENIOR ACTION COUNCIL-NYC

215 West 125th Street, Rm. 400
New York, NY 10027

Phone: 212- 316-9393
Contact: Lani Sanjek, Assoc. Ex. Dir

Office Hours: Mon-Fri, 10am-6pm
Staff: Paid
Geographic Scope: City-wide

Organizational Focus:
Security and dignity for older New
Yorkers and for all ages, including
children.

General Description:
A grassroots membership organization of seniors dedicated to improve
the well-being and health of all older
and younger New Yorkers,
particularly the poor and vulnerable.
Founder of an inter-generational
coalition with statewide Youth
Advocates.

Organizational Resources:
Publications, a Patient's Rights
Hotline, speakers and training on
patient's rights issues and other
action priorities.
Regular Public Meetings: 2nd
Monday of month membership
meeting
Membership Organization?: Yes
Membership Requirement: Dues

Issues:	Constituencies:
Seniors	Seniors
Health Care	Multi-Racial
Social Justice	Disabled people
Children's health needs	

THE NEW YORK STREET THEATRE CARAVAN

161-04 Jamaica Avenue
Jamaica, NY 11432

Phone: 718-657-8070
Contact: Marcia Donalds, Asst. Dir.

Office?: Yes
Staff: Volunteer and paid
Geographic Scope: City-wide

Organizational Focus:
To create high standard of artistic
quality theatre and bring plays of
relevance and social meaning to
audiences not able to afford
commercial events.

General Description:
The NYST Caravan is one of the
original theatres emerging from the
anguish and struggles of the 70s
against the Vietnam War and for civil
rights. Theatre creates dialogue
amongst artists and audiences, raises
questions and shapes a social vision.

Bi-lingual: Spanish

Organizational Resources: News-
letter, videos, and workshops.
Membership Organization?: Yes
Membership Requirements:
Membership in Actors Equity

Issues:	Constituencies:
Arts/Culture	Multi-Racial
Human Rights	Disabled People
Social Justice	Women
Environment	
Women's Rghts	
Workers' Rights	
Foreign Policy	

NICARAGUA SOLIDARITY NETWORK

339 Lafayette Street, #8
New York, NY 10012

Phone: 212-74-9499
Fax: 212-674-9139
Contact: David B. Wilson,

Office?: Yes
Staff: Volunteer
Geographic Scope: City-wide

Organizational Focus:
Providing information on Nicaragua
and Latin America from the
perspective of the left and grassroots
movements.

General Description:
We organize educational events,
work in coalition with Latino and
solidarity groups, and publish the
*Weekly News Update on the
Americas* news summary, which
covers events in Latin America and
the Caribbean. We also provide a
seven-minute weekly radio feed.

Bi-lingual: Spanish

Organizational Resources: News-
letter, update, calendar with Latino
focus, library, database, and speakers.
Membership Organization?: Yes
Membership Requirements:
Interested in NSN goals

Issues:	Constituencies:
Int'l Solidarity	Latino/Hispanic

NORTH AMERICAN CONGRESS ON LATIN AMERICA (NACLA)

475 Riverside Drive, Suite 454
New York, NY 10115

Phone: 212-870-3146
Fax: 212-870-3305
Contact: Pierre Laramee, Exec. Dir.

Office Hours: 9:30am-5:30pm
Staff: Paid

General Description:
The North American Congress on Latin America, founded in 1966, is a research and publishing institute providing in-depth analysis of both US foreign policy toward Latin America and political, social and economic conditions within the region.

Multi-lingual: Spanish, French

Organizational Resources: Bimonthly publication: NACLA Report on the Americas; small research library/reading room on the Americas; speakers, interviews, conferences, etc. For over 25 years, NACLA has offered resources essential to creating critical public awareness of US policies and practices in the region.
Regular Public Meetings: Yes
Membership Organization?: Yes
Membership Requirements:
Subscription to magazine

Issues:	Constituencies:
Int'l Solidarity	Multi-Racial
Media	Activists
Econ. Development	Policy-Makers
Social Justice	Journalists
Anti-Racism	Academics

NOSOTRAS

PO Box 127 Stuyvesant Sta.
New York, NY 10009

Phone: 212-592-3016
Contact: Lisa Napoli
Office?:   No
Staff: None
Geographic Scope: Lower East Side

Organizational Focus:
To promote the economic and social status of women on the Lower East Side.

General Description:
We are a network of women living and working on the Lower East Side who do community organizing around local issues. For example, there are three Boys Clubs in L.E.S. and only one Girls Club; we want to see that change.

Bi-lingual: Spanish mainly

Regular Public Meetings: Once a month
Membership Organization?: Yes
Membership Requirements: Required to attend meetings

Issues:	Constituencies:
Women's Rights	Women
	Latino/Hispanic

NYC GAY & LESBIAN ANTI-VIOLENCE PROJECT

647 Hudson Street
New York, NY 10014

Phone: 212-807-6761
Fax: 212-807-1044
Contact: Matt Foreman, Exec. Dir.

Office Hours: Mon.-Thur. 10-8pm
               Friday 10am-6pm
Staff: Paid and volunteer
Geographic Scope: City-wide

Organizational Focus:
Anti-gay and anti-lesbian bias crime;
domestic violence, sexual assault, and
HIV/AIDS related violence in the
Gay/Lesbian communities.

General Description:
Founded in 1980, AVP serves Lesbian
and Gay crime victims through
counseling, advocacy, information and
referrals. The project serves the
larger community by working to
change public attitudes that tolerate,
insulate or instigate hate-motivated
crime and to reform government
policies and practice affecting Lesbian,
Gay, HIV positive and other crime
survivors.

Bi-lingual: Spanish

Organizational Resources:
Newsletter, pamphlets, 24-hour
hotline, speakers' bureau, organize
protests and a meeting space.
Membership Organization?: No

Issues:	Constituencies:
Anti-Violence	Lesbian/Gay
Lesbian/Gay	Crime Victims
Police Abuse	
HIV/AIDS	
Crime/Criminal Justice	

OPEN HOUSING CENTER, INC.

594 Broadway, Suite 608
New York, NY 10012

Phone: 212-941-6101
Fax: 212-431-7428
Contact: Sylvia Kramer, Ex. Dir.

Office?: Yes
Staff: Paid
Geographic Scope: City-wide

Organizational Focus:
Combating housing discrimination
and finding affordable housing.

General Description:
The Center, in existence for 30
years, assists those facing
discrimination, conducts systemic
tests, and provides information,
testing, and advocacy. Our focus is
on racial discrimination; assistance in
finding affordable housing; and
community outreach and
empowerment education.

Multi-lingual: Spanish

Organizational Resources:
Brochures, workshop facilitators,
counseling, housing information.
Regular Public Meetings: Twice a
year
Membership Organization?: No
"Friends of the Center" membership

Issues:	Constituencies:
Housing/	African American
Homelessness	Caribbean
Education	Multi-Racial
Human Rights	Latino/Hispanic
Anti-Racism	Disabled
Social Justice	

ORGANIZATION OF CHINESE AMERICANS-NYC (OCA)

PO Box 701 Knickerbocker Sta.
New York, NY 10002

Phone: 212-533-8427
Contact: Doris Ling-Cohen, V.P.
Public Affairs

Office?: No
Staff: None
Geographic Scope: City-wide and national

Organizational Focus:
Civil Rights advocacy for Chinese/ Asian Americans

General Description:
OCA is a civil rights organization which advocates for Chinese/Asian Pacific Americans. In doing so, it has worked in coalition with other groups. OCA also offers social and networking opportunities with chapters, and has offered forums on financial issues of interest to Chinese Americans.

Bi-lingual: Chinese

Organizational Resources:
Pamphlets on Immigration Reform Control Act and newsletter.
Regular Public Meetings: Yes
Membership Organization?: Yes
Membership Requirements:
Membership Fee

Issues:	Constituencies:
Anti-Racism	Asian/Pacific
Civil Rights	Islander
Voting Rights	
Immigrants' Rights	

OUT MEDIA

123 Park Place
Brooklyn, NY 11217

Phone: 718-789-1776
Fax: 718-622-6848
Contact: Shelly Weiss

Office Hours: 9am-6pm
Staff: Paid and volunteer
Geographic Scope: City-wide

Organizational Focus:
To increase the positive visibility of Lesbians and Gay men; to empower Gay arts and artists both within our community and in the culture at large.

General Description:
Out Media is a multi-cultural organization committed to celebrate the great diversity of the Lesbian and Gay community through the promotion of cutting edge Queer entertainment and speakers in the broadcasting industry, print media and performance.

Organizational Resources:
Speaker/performers' bureau, workshops facilitators, TV development and production.
Membership Organization?: No

Issues:	Constituencies:
Lesbian/Gay	Lesbian/Gay
Media	
Arts/Culture	
HIV/AIDS	
Social Justice	

OUTRAGE!

PO Box 7045, JAF Station
New York, NY 10116

Phone:	212-969-8724
Fax:	212-647-9824
E-Mail:	Outrage@virtualx.com
Contact:	Jesse Heiwa, Coordinator

Office Hours: Vary
Staff: Volunteer
Geographic Scope: City-wide

Organizational Focus:
Social justice and sexual liberation

General Description:
Outrage is a Queer progressive network that engages in direct actions and study groups. We organized the forum entitled "From Stonewall to Sellout" and the protest at the Intrepid. We are a conspiracy of hope committed to ending oppression against all Queer people while encouraging Queer visibility.

Organizational Resources:
Newsletter, Computer Networking.
Regular Public Meetings: Last Fri. of month
Membership Organization?: No

Issues:	Constituencies:
Lesbian/Gay	Multi-Racial
Social Justice	Lesbian/Gay
Peace/Anti-Militarism	
Anti-Racism	
HIV/AIDS	

OUTSTANDING RENEWAL ENTERPRISES, INC.

PO Box 20488 Tompkins Sq. Sta.
New York, NY 10009

Phone:	212-420-0621
Fax:	212-673-1467
Contact:	Christina Datz, Director
Office?:	No
Staff:	Volunteer

Geographic Scope: Manhattan, parts of B'klyn

Organizational Focus:
Recycling and composting, environmental education and street tree care.

General Description:
At the Lower East Side Ecology Center, located on East 7th Street between Ave B and C, we accept: household batteries, compost, white office and computer paper, scrap metal and textiles for recycling. Hours: Wed. seasonal; Fri., Sat., and Sunday 8am-5pm year round. Compostable Collection at Union Square Green Market Wed. & Sat. 9am-5pm year round. We also have a "Tree Team" which works on street trees.

Multi-lingual: Spanish, Chinese, German

Organizational Resources:
Newsletter, compost workshops and general recycling and waste prevention information. Tours/workshops for school groups.
Membership Organization?: Yes

Issues:	Constituencies:
Environment	Multi-Racial
Education	
Econ. Development	
Arts/Culture	

PALESTINE AID SOCIETY

PO Box 2724
New York, NY 10008

Phone: 212-385-4233
Fax: Same/Call first
Contact: Emad Qadi, Chapter
            Coordinator

Office Hours: Wed. 4:30-9pm &
               Sat./Sun. 8am-2pm
Staff: Volunteer
Geographic Scope: City-wide

Organizational Focus:
To provide direct material aid to self
help projects in the occupied
territories -- child care and nursery
centers and to promote peace and
justice in the Middle East.

General Description:
P.A.S. was founded in 1978 at a time
when Palestinian society was under
occupation; P.A.S. helps ensure
community survival and cultural
identity.

Multi-lingual: Arabic, Russian &
Spanish

Organizational Resources:
Speakers' bureau, pamphlets, videos
newsletter
Regular Public Meetings: Every
Wednesday at 6 pm.
Membership Organization?: Yes
Membership Requirements: Believe in
Palestinian cause and peace and
justice in Mid-East.

Issues: Constituencies:
Int'l Solidarity   Palestinian/
Anti-Racism   Middle
Human Rights   Eastern

THE PANEL

121 6th Avenue, Suite 507
New York, NY 10013

Phone: 212-226-1330
Fax: 212-274-0294
Contact: Rob Jones, Exec. Dir.

Office Hours: 9am-5pm
Staff: Paid
Geographic Scope: City-wide

Organizational Focus:
Cultural diversity and intergroup
relations.

General Description:
The Panel is an organization devoted
to fostering cultural diversity and
awareness through interactive
workshops for youth and adults. The
Panel's mission is to empower people
to become more effective and
responsible citizens and help them
learn the requisite skills to function
harmoniously in an increasingly multi-
cultural and multi-ethnic city.

Organizational Resources:
We have a youth workers training to
teach the techniques we use with
youth. We also have a staff of
experienced facilitators and trainers
who can be helpful with workshop
design and meeting facilitation.
Membership Organization?: No

Issues: Constituencies:
Anti-Racism   Youth
Arts/Culture
Anti-Violence

PAPER TIGER TV

339 Lafayette Street
New York, NY 10012

Phone: 212 420-9045
Fax: 212-420-8223
Contact: Susan Levine

Office Hours: Mon-Thurs. 12-6pm
Staff: Paid
Geographic Scope: City-wide

Organizational Focus:
Paper Tiger TV is a video collective
which produces and programs shows
on public access TV in NYC.

General Description:
The collective produces work around
social and political issues with a
particular focus on media literacy,
representation and media equity.

Bi-lingual: Spanish

Organizational Resources:
Videos, media literacy, workshops,
activist books
Membership Organization?: No

Issues:
Media
Education

PARENTS COALITION FOR EDUCATION IN NEW YORK CITY

24-16 Bridge Plaza Sq. #404
Long Island City , New York 11107

Phone: 718-937-1119
Fax: 718-937-8217
Contact: Jon Moscow, Exec. Dir.

Office Hours: Mon-Fri, 9am-5pm
Staff: Paid
Geographic Scope: City-wide

Organizational Focus:
Improving New York City public
schools through parent
empowerment, citywide membership
organization of public school parents
and parent groups. Our purpose is
,to create the condition for
educational success for all NYC
public school students through
parent empowerment.

Multi-lingual: Spanish, Chinese and
Creole

Organizational Resources:
Newsletter, workshops, speakers'
bureau
Regular Public Meetings: quarterly
membership meetings
Membership Requirements: School
or community-based parent group,
individual parents or a community
member who shares organization's
goals.

Issues: Constituencies:
Education   Parents
Youth   Multi-Racial
Anti-Racism

PARODNECK FOUNDATION FOR SELF HELP HOUSING & COMMUNITY DEVELOPMENT, INC.

121 Sixth Avenue, Suite 501
New York NY 10013

Phone: 212-431-9700
Fax: 212-431-9783
Contact: Rebecca Dib, Housing
           Specialist

Office Hours: 9am-5pm
Staff: Paid
Geographic Scope: City-wide

Organizational Focus:
Self-help housing, community
development, planning; low income
housing advocacy, "community
building."

General Description:
The Parodneck Foundation provides
financial and technical assistance to
self help housing, planning,
environmental, and community
development efforts throughout
New York City.

Bi-lingual: Spanish

Organizational Resources: In Rem
organizer's sourcebook and
newsletter.

Issues:	Constituencies:
Housing/	High School/
Homelessness	College Students
Social Justice	
Education	
Environment	

PARTIDO INDEPENDENTISTA PUERTORRIQUENO

PO Box 1481 Gracie Station
New York, NY 10028

Phone: 212-860-7655
Contact: Juan Rodriquez, Co-Pres.

Office: No
Staff: Volunteer
Geographic Scope: City-wide

Organizational Focus:
Independence of P.R. by means of the
electoral process and negotiation
with the US Congress.

General Description:
Our national party, established in
1946, has its main offices in Puerto
Rico. We have officially been
established here since 1993 to
organize the thousands of Puerto
Ricans who favor independence and
to build solidarity among the
progressive, liberal and leftist organizations in NY and the US in general.

Bi-lingual: Spanish

Organizational Resource: A newspaper *El Antillano*; speakers and
workshops informing about the
history, politics, culture and struggles
of Puerto Ricans.
Regular Public Meeting: Every two
months.
Membership Organization?:Yes
Membership Requirement:
Committed to the peaceful struggle
for P.R. independence and to the
polices and position of our party.

Issue:	Constituencies:
Social Justice	Latino/Hispanic
Anti Racism	Caribbean
Anti-Violence	Multi-Racial

PEOPLE ABOUT CHANGING EDUCATION

115 West 28 Street, Suite 3R
New York, NY 10001

Phone: 212-643-8490
Fax: 212-643-7867
Contact: Don Murphy, Coordinator

Office Hours: 10:30am-6pm
Staff: Paid and volunteer
Geographic Scope: City-wide

Organizational Focus:
Pro-equality reform of NYC public schools.

General Description:
Multi-racial network of parents, educators and students that works in coalitions for multicultural education to encompass race, class, ethnicity, nationality, gender, sexual orientation and disability. We organize forums and workshops for teachers and community groups, produce curricula and publish *School Voices* .

Multi-lingual: Spanish, Chinese, French

Organizational Resources:
Newsletter, *Malcolm X Study Guide*, *School Voices* newspaper, public forums and educational workshops
Regular Public Meetings: Public forum 3-4 times a year.
Membership Organization?: Yes
Membership Requirements: Annual Dues

Issues:	Constituencies:
Education	NYC Public
Youth	School
	Parents
	Students
	Teachers

PEOPLE'S DECADE OF HUMAN RIGHTS EDUCATION, INC.

526 West 111th Street, Suite 4e
New York, NY 10025

Phone: 212-749-3156
Fax: 212-666-6325
Contact: Shulamit Koenig, Exec. Dir

Office Hours: 24 hours a day
Staff: Paid and volunteer
Geographic Scope: City-wide

Organizational Focus:
Promoting advocacy and training in human rights education thematically and regionally world-wide.

General Description:
Promotion, networking, training of trainers, sharing and development of materials, informal and nonformal human rights education as it relates to social development and people's daily lives in all sectors of society.

Multi-lingual: Spanish, French, German, Hebrew & Arabic

Organizational Resources:
Training materials, trainers, resource people, speakers, newsletter
Membership Organization?: No

Issues:
Human Rights
Education
Anti-Racism
Int'l Solidarity
Social Justice

PREGONES THEATER

700 Grand Concourse
Bronx, NY 10451

Phone: 718-585-1202
Fax: 718-585-1608
Contact: Rosalba Rolon, Artistic
            Director

Office Hours: 9:30am-5:30pm &
              weekends
Geographic Scope: City-wide

General Description:
Pregones Theater, based in the South
Bronx, was founded as a touring
company 16 years ago, its title being
a Spanish word for "street vendors'
cries." Our mission is to create
innovative and challenging theater, of
the highest quality possible, rooted in
Puerto Rican traditions and popular
artistic expressions; and to present
performing artists from diverse
cultures with the aim of offering
Latino and other communities an
artistic means to question, reaffirm
and enhance our roles in society.

Bi-lingual: Spanish

Regular Public Meetings?: No
Membership Organization?: No

Issues: Constituencies:
Arts/Culture   Latino/Hispanic

PRENATAL CARE STEERING COMMITTEE

30 Third Avenue, Room 619
Brooklyn, NY 11217

Phone: 718-875-7893
Fax: 718-797-1254
Contact: Judi Clark, Director

Office Hours: Monday, Wed. &
                Thurs. 11am-5pm
Staff: Paid
Geographic Scope: City-wide

Organizational Focus:
To ensure quality health care to poor
and working poor women and their
children.

General Description:
Health education advocacy groups
working to improve the quality of
health provided to pregnant women
and their children.

Organizational Resources:
Pamphlets, speakers bureau, and
workshop facilitators.
Regular Public Meetings: 3rd
Wednesday, 3-5pm 225 Broadway
17th fl.
Membership Organization?: Yes,
individuals $35, organizations $45
yearly.

Issues: Constituencies:
Gov't Accountability Women
Health Care   Youth
Women's' Rights
Education

PROFESSOR LOUIE PRODUCTIONS
399 14th Street
Brooklyn, NY 11215

Phone: 718-768-8728
Contact: Professor Louie

Office: No
Staff: None
Geographic Scope: City-wide

General Description:
The poets of the street: performers who say a lot about the city and the world we live in and who speak in a voice that can be heard and understood by everyday people in all the different communities of NYC.

Organizational Resources:
We perform at rallies, benefits, block parties, meetings, conferences, forums, etc. Tapes available.
Membership Organization: No

Issues: Constituencies:
Arts/Culture   Multi-Racial
Social Justice
Education

PROJECT CURE!
383 Kingston Avenue, Suite 213
Brooklyn, NY 11213

Phone: 718-323-9291
Fax: Same
Contact: Dr. Laz, Director

Office Hours: 9am-6pm
Staff: Volunteer
Geographic scope: Crown Heights

Organizational Focus:
Project Cure! is essentially a volunteer community based effort made up of Blacks and Jews of Crown Heights, B'klyn.

General Description:
Project Cure! sponsors a variety of meaningful activities to foster racial harmony and positive communication. These programs include joint basketball/sports events; multi-cultural celebration; dialogues to understanding; art murals; and a Black-Jewish music group.

Organizational Resources:
Newsletter, videos, speakers, articles and pamphlets
Regular Public Meetings: Three times each month
Membership Organization?: No

Issues: Constituencies:
Anti-Racism   Multi-Racial
Multi-culturalism   Jewish
Youth   African American
Education   Caribbean
Environment

PROJECT REACH

1 Orchard Street, 2nd Floor
New York, NY 10002

Phone: 212-966- 4227
Fax: 212-966-4963
Contact: Don Kao

Office Hours: Mon.-Fri. 10am-6pm
Staff: Paid
Geographic Scope: City-wide

Organizational Focus:
To provide opportunities where
young people can better understand
the systems/institutions that
disempower them and organize with
other young people to change the
conditions that oppress them

General Description:
Project Reach is a youth and adult-
multiracial community-based group
providing services such as crisis
intervention counseling, advocacy and
a youth organizing center training
young people as peer counselors.

Multi-lingual: Spanish and Chinese

Organizational Resources: Meeting
space, workshop facilitators,
speakers, technical assistance, and a
toll free number, 1-800-70-REACH
Membership Organization?: No

Issues: Constituencies:
Anti-Racism   Multi-Racial
                     Youth
                     Lesbian/Gay

PUBLIC MEDIA, INC.

330 West 42nd Street, #2410
New York, NY 10036

Phone: 212-947-1395
Fax: 212-643-1208
Contact: Eugene Aleinikoff

Staff: Volunteer
Geographic Scope: City-wide

Organizational Focus:
Fiscal management for television
productions by independents

General Description:
Independent producers of television
documentaries are in Public Media
Inc. to help facilitate productions
receiving grants from foundations and
individuals.

Membership Organization?: No

Issues:
Media
Education

PUEBLO EN MARCHA, INC.

401 East 145th Street
Bronx, NY 10454

Phone: 718-665-7375
Contact: Maximino Rivera, Exec.
Director

Office Hours: 9am-5pm
Staff: Paid and volunteer
Geographic Scope: Community Bd.
#1 area in the Bronx

Organizational Focus:
The group is dedicated to the
betterment of the community at
large in the areas of housing, youth
and emergency food services for
families and the elderly.

General Description:
Services include: information,
referral and assistance, housing and
social service advocacy, emergency
food (pantry), and clothing referrals.
The neighborhood Youth Alliance
Program is run by the Youth
Advisory Council.

Bi-lingual: Spanish

Organizational Resources:
Housing workshops, meeting space,
pamphlets.
Regular Public Meetings: Call for
schedule
Membership Organization?: No

Issues:	Constituencies:
Housing/	Youth
Homelessness	African American
Youth	Latino/Hispanic

PUERTO RICAN LEGAL DEFENSE AND EDUCATION FUND

99 Hudson Street, Suite 1401
New York, NY 10013

Phone: 212-219-3360
800-328-2322
Fax: 212-431-4276
Contact: Juan A. Figueroa, Pres. &
General Counsel

Office Hours: 9am-5pm
Staff: Paid
Geographic Scope: City-wide

Organizational Focus:
PRLDEF exists to ensure that all
Puerto Rican and other Latinos are
guaranteed the opportunity to
succeed. Through advocacy, education and litigation, PRLDEF seeks to
secure and safeguard the political,
economic, social and legal rights of
our community.

General Description:
PRLDEF protects civil rights, ensures
political access and fights poverty and
discrimination faced by Latinos. We
work for improvements in education,
public employment, housing, health care,
and minority access to law school and
we train civil rights lawyers.

Bi-lingual: Spanish

Organizational Resources: Newsletter, pamphlets, meeting space,
speakers, compilation of job
announcements. Legal referral
service.
Membership Organization?: No

Issues:	Constituencies:
Human Rights	Latino/Hispanic
Civil Rights	

QUEENS COALITION FOR POLITICAL ALTERNATIVES

64-64 229th Street
Flushing, NY 11364

Phone: 718-229-4201
Fax: 718-279-2456
Contact: Lois Marbach, Chair

Office?:   No
Staff: None
Geographic Scope: Queens

Organizational Focus:
Issue forums, voter registration, issue street activity, lobbying, campaign assistance.

General Description:
Boroughwide coalition of groups and individuals working on social justice, labor, civil rights, anti-bias and electoral reform issues. Support for progressive candidates.

Multi-lingual: Brochures in Spanish, Korean & Chinese

Organizational Resources: Newsletter, issue information distribution, candidate support and volunteer activities, assistance lobbying, phoning.
Regular Public Meetings: Sept.-May, 4th Mon., 7:30pm at CUNY Law School
Membership Organization?: Yes
Membership Requirements:
Suggested dues of $15/$10 seniors and students

Issues:	Constituencies:
Anti-Racism	Multi-Racial
Social Justice	Senior
Women's Rights	Lesbian/Gay
Workers' Rights	Disabled People
	Women

QUEENS WOMEN'S CENTER

Queensborough Hall, Rm. 209
120-55 Queens Boulevard
Kew Gardens, NY 11424

Phone: 718-793-0672
Fax: Same/Call first
Contact: Ann J. Jawin, Chair, Board
          of Directors

Office Hours: Usually Monday-
                Friday 9am-5pm
Staff: Volunteer
Geographic Scope: Queens

Multi-lingual: Spanish, Chinese and Russian (various volunteer staff)

Organizational Resources:
Newsletter, small meeting room, hotline, job club, workshops, support group, general informational meetings.
Regular Public Meetings: 2nd Thursday of every month and a yearly conference.
Membership Organization?:Yes
Membership Requirements: $25 annual dues. Meetings are all open.

Issues:	Constituencies:
Women's Rights	Women
Econ. Development	
Education	
Crime/Criminal Justice	
Reproductive Rights	

QUEENSBORO COUNCIL FOR SOCIAL WELFARE

221-10 Jamaica Avenue
Queens Village, NY 11428

Phone: 718-468-8025
Fax: 718-464-8811
Contact: Joan Sarrano Laufer, Exec.
             Director

Office Hours: Mon.-Fri. 9am-5pm
Staff: Paid and volunteer
Geographic Scope: Queens

Organizational Focus:
QCSW is a council of Queens human
services agencies and groups.

General Description:
Provides information and referrals,
technical assistance, training,
education and housing assistance.

Multi-lingual: Spanish and Hindi

Organizational Resources: Newsletter, speakers' bureau, meeting
space, pamphlets, training, and
technical assistance.
Regular Public Meetings: Periodic
Membership Organization?: Yes
Membership Requirements:

Issues: Constituencies:
Welfare Advocacy   Seniors
Immigrants' Rights   Queens County
                        Residents

RACISM JUST UNDO IT

PO Box 1103 Cooper Station
New York, NY 10276

Phone: 212-465-3150
Contact: Tavoria Kellam

Office?:   No
Staff: Volunteer
Geographic Scope: City-wide

Organizational Focus:
RJUI is a task force dedicated to
raising the first generation of
prejudice-free New Yorkers.

General Description:
We're working toward this goal by:
educating people on the rights and
responsibilities necessary to create a
prejudice-free society, and creating
projects that help people un-learn
racism.

Organizational Resources:
Pamphlets, Hotline (212-465-3150)
speakers' bureau
Membership Organization?: No

Issues:
Anti-Racism

RADIO BANDUNG

220 Manhattan Ave. Suite 5R
New York, NY 10025

Phone: 212 316-3121
Fax: 212-316-3121
Contact: Wesley Maczivili,
           Workshop Coordinator.

Office: No
Staff: Volunteer
Geographic Scope: City-wide

Organizational Focus:
Radio Bandung broadcasts the voices,
concerns, music and poetry of the
Asian Pacific Diaspora and seeks to
build a forum for multi-racial voices.

General Description:
Radio Bandung is a radio collective
that produces a weekly evening
newsmagazine every Monday night
from 10pm-11pm on WBAI/Pacifica
Radio (99.5 FM).

Multi-lingual: Chinese, Tagalog,
Korean

Organizational Resources: Speakers'
bureau, training workshops,
audiotapes and newsletter.
Membership organization?: No

Issues: Constituencies
Media   Asian/Pacific
Arts/Culture   Islander
                     Multi-Racial

RED HOOK ARTS

402 Van Brunt Street
Brooklyn, NY 11231

Phone: 718-852-8058
Fax: Same
Contact: Dorothy Randall Gray,
           Executive Director

Office Hours: 10am-6pm
Staff: Paid
Geographic Scope: Red Hook

General Description:
Red Hook Arts is a not for profit
youth organization utilizing the visual
and performing arts to educate,
empower and enrich the community.
For more than 14 years, we have
provided leadership and conflict
resolution training, free arts
programs, and positive alternatives.

Organizational Resources: Pamphlets
and brochures
Regular Public Meetings: Bimonthly
Membership Organization?: No

Issues: Constituencies:
Youth   Youth
Arts/Culture   Latino/Hispanic
Education   African American

REPO HISTORY

339 Lafayette Street, 301
New York, NY 10012

Fax: 212-925-2241
Contact: Tom Klein 212-431-4059
Lisa Maya Knauer
212-533-3032
Staff: None
Geographic Scope: City-wide

Organizational Focus:
Using art for social change

General Description:
We are a collective of artists,
writers, educators and organizers.
Through site-specific public art, performances, installations, and community collaborations, we question
how history is constructed, challenge
the official version, and insert stories,
people and events which have been
omitted or marginalized because of
class, race, gender or sexuality.

Organizational Resources: Meeting
space; speakers on public art, art and
activism, etc.; advice on doing public
art or community history projects.
Regular Public Meetings?: Yes
Membership Organization?: Yes
Membership Requirements:
Willingness to share in administrative
work; attendance at meetings.

Issues:	Constituencies:
Arts/Culture	Multi-Racial
Anti-Racism	
Economic Development	
Education	
Housing/Homelessness	
Lesbian/Gay	
Reproductive Rights	
Social Justice	

REFORUM: A CITY JOURNAL FOR SOCIAL CHANGE

PO Box 1028 Church St. Station
New York, NY 10003

Phone: 212- 420-1959
Fax: 212- 529-4666
Contact: David Dring, Contact

Office Hours: None
Staff: Volunteer
Geographic Scope: City-wide

Organizational Focus:
Reforum publishes social
commentary in order to generate
dialogue and catalyze political change.

General Description:
Reforum is a forum for writers and
artists to comment critically about
the work that they do, current
societal issues, public policy. By
encouraging the articulation and
development of progressive thought
and social commentary, the journal
nurtures fresh perspectives.

Organizational Resources:
Workshop facilitators to develop
writing skills.

RIPTIDE COMMUNICATIONS

666 Broadway, Suite 444
New York, NY 10012

Phone: 212-260-5000
Contact: David Lerner, VP

Office Hours: 10am-6pm
Staff: Paid
Geographic Scope: City-wide

Organizational Focus:
Public relations for progressive
groups and individuals.

General Description:
Advocacy on behalf of clients to the
press. Message development and
training in media relations.

Bi-lingual: Spanish

Regular Public Meetings?: No
Membership Organization?: No

Issues:
Media
Organizational Development

RISE AND SHINE PRODUCTIONS

300 West 453rd Street, 4th Fl
New York, NY 10036

Phone: 212-265-5909
Fax: 212-265-3722
Contact: Devorah Hill,
           Coordinating Dir.

Office Hours: 9am-5pm & often
                evenings
Staff: Paid
Geographic Scope: Manhattan

Organizational Focus:
To put media in the hands of the
community, specifically young people.
We act as a conduit for the self
expression of youth.

General Description:
Media education group. We work in
community and school settings
teaching media awareness and video
production. Rise & Shine is a grant
recipient of Manhattan
Neighborhood Network. As a
grantee, R&S runs ongoing
workshops in video production.
Workshops are open to Harlem,
Clinton and Chelsea residents.

Bi-lingual: Spanish

Organizational Resources:
Videos; youth producers are available
for speaking and workshop
facilitating; meeting space.
Regular Public Meetings: No
Membership Organization?: No

Issues:	Constituencies:
Media	Youth
Youth	Students

SAKHI FOR SOUTH ASIAN WOMEN

PO Box 20208, Greeley Sq. Sta.
New York, NY 10001

Phone: 212-695-5447
Fax: 212-564-8745
Contact: Prema Vora, Program
         Coordinator

Office Hours: Mon.-Fri. 10am-6pm
Staff: Paid
Geographic Scope: City-wide

Organizational Focus:
SAKHI is a South Asian Women's
organization that works to break the
silence around violence against
women in the community through
individual advocacy and community
outreach and organizing.

General Description:
SAKHI provides emotional support
and referrals for social services,
coordinates legal clinics, conducts
English classes, and organizes
domestic workers against abusive
conditions.

Multi-lingual: Hindi/Urdu, Punjabi,
Bengali, Gujarati

Organizational Resources:
Newsletter, video on domestic
violence, workshops/presentations
Membership Organization?: No

Issues: Constituencies:
Women's Rights   Women
Immigrants' Rights   South Asian
Workers' Rights
Anti-Violence

SANG-FROID, LTD. (DYKE TV)

588 Broadway, Suite 504
New York, NY 10012

Phone: 212 343 9335
Fax: 212-343 9337
Contact: Linda Chapman, Executive
         Producer.

Office Hours: Mon.-Fri. 10am-6pm
Staff: Paid and volunteer
Geographic Scope: City-wide

Organizational Focus:
Multi-cultural and inter-disciplinary
artistic collaborations with
Lesbian/Gay focus.

General Description:
Sang-Froid is the producing
organization for Dyke T.V., the
stylish and dynamic weekly T.V.
magazine by and for the national
Lesbian community, currently airing
in more than twenty-five cities across
the country.

Organizational Resources: Dyke TV
video tapes and merchandise.
Membership Organization?: No

Issues: Constituencies:
Media   Women
Lesbian/Gay   Lesbians/Gays
Performance   Multi-Racial

SINGLE PARENT RESOURCE CENTER

141 West 28th Street #302
New York, NY 10001

Phone: 212-947-0221
Fax: 212-947-0369
Contact: Suzanne Y. Jones, Exec.
            Director

Office Hours: Monday-Friday
               9:30am-5:30pm
Staff: Paid
Geographic Scope: City-wide

Organizational Focus:
Direct service provider, advocate and
educational force for single parents
and their children, primarily in NYC.

General Description:
Provides support and referral
services (group and individual
counseling), to low income and
homeless parents and children, and
women in and released from prison.
Trains professionals in other
organizations to form groups for
single parents.

Organizational Resources: Newsletter, meeting space, pamphlets,
speakers, and workshop facilitators.
Membership Organization?: No

Issues: Constituencies:
Youth   Single parents &
                     their children

SISTERS ON STAGE

c/o Lesbian/Gay Community Ctr.
208 West 13th Street
New York, NY 10011

Phone: 212-691-0722 (12-5pm)
Contact: Janis Astor del Valle, Co-
            founder

Office: No
Staff: None
Geographic Scope: City-wide

General Description:
Sisters On Stage is a not-for-profit
multi-cultural organization of
professional playwrights, actors and
directors from the lesbian
community. We present original
work, but our main objective is to
develop a mentoring program for
lesbians who aspire to be playwrights
in the professional theater.

Multi-lingual: Spanish and French

Organizational Resources:
Referrals/networking for lesbian
theater professionals/productions.
Liaison between above and lesbian
community.

Issues: Constituencies:
Arts/Culture   Multi-Cultural/
Lesbian   Multi-Ethnic
                     Lesbian

SKYLIGHT PICTURES, INC.

330 W. 42nd Street, 2410
New York, NY 10036

Phone: 212-947-5333
Fax: 212-947-5401
Contact: Peter Kinoy, Partner

Office Hours: 9:30am-6pm
Staff: No
Geographic Scope: City-wide; national

Organizational Focus:
To produce and distribute
independent media in collaboration
with social struggle.

General Description:
Video production company
specializing in social documentaries.
Extensive history of work with poor
people's movements.

Bi-lingual: Spanish

Organizational Resources: We have
videos, sometimes provide editing
facilities, document events etc.
Membership Organization?: No

Issues:
Media
Youth
Housing/Homelessness
Arts/Culture

SOCIAL ACTION COMMITTEE

c/o Community Church of NY
40 East 35th Street
New York, NY 10016

Phone: 718-920-4576
Fax: 212-683-4998
Contact: Leonore Tiefer

Office?:   No
Staff: None
Geographic Scope: City-wide

Organizational Focus:
Support a broad progressive agenda.

General Description:
Committee of a church that supports
progressive political action such as:
letter writing, phoning, demonstrations and other support.

Organizational Resources: Human
resources - volunteers available
Regular Public Meetings: 3rd. Sun.
September-May 1-2pm
Membership Organization?: No

Issues: Constituencies:
Social Justice   Multi-Racial
Human Rights
Health Care
Reproductive Rights

SOCIALIST PARTY - USA
516 West 25th Street, #404
New York, NY 10001

Phone: 212-691-0776
Fax: Same/Call first
Contact: Kari Fisher, Co-Chair

Office Hours: 12-7pm
Staff: Volunteer
Geographic Scope: National

Organizational Focus:
Independent political party

General Description:
We are democratic socialists striving
to establish a radical democracy that
places people's lives under their own
control -- a non-racist, feminist,
socialist society in which people
cooperate at work, at home, and in
the community.

Multi-lingual: Spanish, German,
French

Organizational Resources:
Newsletter, pamphlets, videos,
speakers, and workshop facilities
Regular Public Meetings: Monthly
Membership Organization?: Yes
Membership Requirements: Sliding
Dues

Issues:	Constituencies
Social Justice	Multi-Racial
Human Rights	
Gov't Accountability	
Anti-Racism	
Peace/Anti-Militarism	

SOJOURNER TRUTH ADOLESCENT RITES SOCIETY
PO Box 5587 Manhattanville St.
New York, NY 10027

Phone: 212-928-5165
Contact: Gwendolyn Gilyard, Pres.

Office?: No
Staff: None
Geographic Scope: City-wide

Organizational Focus:
Helping youth, particularly girls, to
become viable leaders/citizens
through the rites of passage process.

General Description:
Our work includes: year long training
program for adolescent girls in
positive subjects not taught in school;
serving as a resource and service
center for other groups and parents
wanting to learn the rites of passage
process and procedures.

Organizational Resources:
Newsletter, pamphlets, a speakers'
bureau, a manual, workshop
facilitators and some videos for
borrowing.
Regular Public Meetings: Bi-yearly
conference
Membership Organization?: Yes
Membership Requirements: $25
yearly dues

Issues:	Constituencies:
Youth	African American
Education	Caribbean
	Women
	Youth

SOUTH ASIAN AIDS ACTION (SAAA)

PO Box 1326, Peter Stuyvesant Sta.
New York, NY 10009

Phone: 212-239-1451 ext. 6126

Office: None
Staff: Volunteer
Geographic Scope: City-wide

Organizational Focus:
HIV/AIDS education and outreach in
NY metro area's South Asian
communities.

General Description:
An all-volunteer organization which
distributes HIV/AIDS information in 7
languages, in South Asian neighborhoods and at community events; has
outreach projects for South Asian
women, students, taxi-drivers, etc.,
conducts workshops and provides
referrals to health care professionals
and social workers for persons of
South Asian descent who are living
with or affected by HIV/AIDS.

Multi-lingual: Hindi, Pujabi, Urdu,
Malayalam, Tamil, Chinese, Gujarati

Organizational Resources: HIV/AIDS
educational pamphlets available in
English, Hindi, Urdu, etc... speakers
and workshop facilitators;
translation/language support
Regular Public Meetings: Every
second Wed., call for details
Membership Organization?: No

Issues: Constituencies:
HIV/AIDS   People of South
Human Rights   Asian descent
Immigrants' Rights
Int'l Solidarity

SOUTH BRONX CLEAN AIR COALITION

2432 Grand Concourse #504
Bronx, NY 10458

Phone: 718-365-5071
Fax: 718-584-3258
Contact: Nina Laboy, Co-Chair

Office Hours: 9am-5pm
Staff: Volunteer
Geographic Scope: South Bronx

General Description:
The South Bronx Clean Air Coalition
is a grassroots group of over 60
active volunteers with more than 800
participants. Local schools,
community-based organizations and
civil rights organizations make up this
coalition whose goal is to fight
environmental and economic racism
through education on issues of
sustainable development and
community organizing.

Bi-lingual: Spanish

Organizational Resources:
Environmental justice library, meeting
space until 8:30pm, and speakers.
Regular Public Meetings: Third Thurs.
of every month
Membership Organization?: No

Issues: Constituencies:
Environment   Multi-Racial
Gov't Accountability   Low Income
Social Justice
Sustainable Development
Econ. Development

SOUTHSIDE TELEVISION
378 Manhattan Avenue, #2R
Brooklyn, NY 11211

Phone: 718-389-8354
Fax: 718-719-5874
Contact: Robert Wyrod,
Coordinator

Office: No
Staff: Volunteer
Geographic Scope: Williamsburg,
Brooklyn

Organizational Focus:
To provide training and opportunities
for video production to members of
Williamsburg community.

General Description:
Southside Television is a community-
based video collective in
Williamsburg, Brooklyn. We train
members of the community in video
production while making videos of
social and cultural importance.

Bi-lingual: Spanish

Organizational Resources: Many
videos (interviews, documentaries,
dramas) are available to anyone.
Regular Public Meetings: Regular
public screenings
Membership Requirements: Members
should live, work or have some
connection to Williamsburg

Issues:	Constituencies:
Media	Latino/Hispanic
Social Justice	
HIV/AIDS	
Anti-Racism	
Arts/Culture	
Education	

STATEN ISLAND COALITION FOR SURVIVAL
PO Box 469
Staten Island, NY 10314

Phone: 718-979-6563
Fax: 718-667-4740

Office Hours: Irregular
Staff: Volunteer
Geographic Scope: Staten Island and
some of Brooklyn

Organizational Focus:
Coalition of progressive groups.

General Description:
Provides office, TV, and services to
member organizations.

Organizational Resources:
Newsletter, videos -- we produce
two shows weekly.
Regular Public Meetings: Yes
Membership Organization?: Yes
Membership Requirements: Yearly
Dues

Issues:	Constituencies:
Peace/	Multi-Racial
Anti-Militarism	
Social Justice	
Anti-Racism	
Int'l Solidarity	

STATEN ISLAND COUNCIL FOR PEACE AND JUSTICE

PO Box 509
Staten Island, NY 10314

Phone: 718-979-6563
Fax: 718-667-4740
Contact: Angelo D'Angelo, Chair

Office?:   No
Staff: None
Geographic Scope: Staten Island

Organizational Focus:
Anti-war; anti-draft; and pro-justice.

General Description:
We conduct educational forums on world peace, Haiti, Panama etc.

Organizational Resources:
Newsletter
Regular Public Meetings: Sporadic
Membership Organization?: Yes
Membership Requirements: Yearly Membership

Issues:
Peace/Anti-Militarism
Environment
Gov't Accountability

STRYCKER'S BAY NEIGHBORHOOD COUNCIL

109 West 88th Street - Basement
New York, NY 10024

Phone: 212-874-7272
Fax: 212-721-5314
Contact: Kelley Williams, Director

Office?:   Yes
Staff: Paid
Geographic Scope: Upper West Side

Organizational Focus:
Eviction prevention, tenant organizing, housing and entitlement advocacy, information and assistance.

General Description:
SBNC provides eviction prevention, housing and entitlement advocacy on a walk-in basis to low and moderate income residents of the Community Board #7 area.

Bi-lingual: Spanish

Organizational Resources:
Newsletter
Membership Organization?: No

Issues:	Constituencies:
Housing/	Low/Moderate
Homelessness	Income residents
Welfare Advocacy	

STUDENTS ORGANIZING STUDENTS (SOS)

1600 Broadway, Suite 404
New York, NY 10019

Phone: 212-977-6710
Fax: 212-489-7355
Contact: Anna Maria Nieves,
            Director of Programs

Office Hours: Mon.-Fri. 10am-6pm
Staff: Paid
Geographic Scope: City-wide and national

Organizational Focus:
We advocate for young women's health through training young women to become leaders in their communities.

General Description:
A national network of high school & college-aged women who advocate and organize for young women's health. We do this through several programs: skills program (high school level), field organizer program (college level), and internship program (high school and college).

Multi-lingual: Cantonese, Mandarin

Organizational Resources: Newsletters, speakers, workshop facilitators
Regular Public Meetings: Once every 2 weeks.
Membership Organization?: Yes

Issues: Constituencies:
Health   Women
Women's Rights   Youth
Reproductive Rights   Multi-Racial
Anti-Violence   Lesbian/Gay
Youth

SUB SAHARA AIDS RESCUE, INC.

185 Parkhill Avenue, Suite LB
Staten Island, NY 10304

Contact: Esther Okoye, Program
            Coordinator

Office Hours: None
Geographic Scope: Staten Island

General Description:
SSAR, a nonprofit organization is initiating a campaign to combat the spread of AIDS among people of African descent. We believe that all people of color need to be fully educated in a culturally sensitive environment about the deadly HIV virus which can drastically change their lives and the lives of their loved ones.

Multi-lingual: Francais, Swahili, Arabic, Hausa Ibo, Yoruba, Twi, etc.

Organizational Resources:
Translation/interpretation in various African languages.
Regular Public Meetings: Bi-monthly
Membership Organization?: No

Issues: Constituencies:
HIV/AIDS   African Natives

TAHRIR: VOICES OF THE ARAB WORLD

505 8th Avenue
New York, NY 10018

Phone: 212-279-0707
Fax: 212-564-5359
Contact: Barbara Nimri Aziz,
          Producer

Office Hours: Flexible
Geographic Scope: City-wide

Organizational Focus:
A radio production team designed to present material for and about the Arab-American community.

General Description:
Based at WBAI Pacifica Radio, Tahrir produces programming for both local and national distribution, and does outreach into the Arab community. We also recruit and train new producers.

Organizational Resources: Speakers bureau, fliers and pamphlets.
Regular Public Meetings?: No
Membership Organization?: Yes

Issues:	Constituencies:
Media	Multi-Racial
Arts/Culture	Palestinian/
Immigrants' Rights	Middle Eastern
Social Justice	

THEATER FOR THE NEW CITY

155 First Avenue
New York, NY 10003

Phone: 212-254-1190
Fax: 212-475-0108
Contact: Joy Linscheid,
          Administrator

Office Hours: 11 am-6pm
Staff: Paid and Volunteer
Geographic Scope: City-wide

General Description:
We are a writers' theater. We do 30-40 new productions a year plus a huge community outreach program including arts-in-education and an annual summer street theater which performs for free in all five boroughs of New York.

Bi-lingual: Spanish

Organizational Resources: Meeting space, performance and rehearsal spaces.
Membership Organization?: No

Issues:	Constituencies:
Art/Culture	Multi-Racial
Youth	Youth
Anti-Violence	
Education	
Anti-Racism	

THEATER OF THE OPPRESSED LABORATORY

Brecht Forum
122 West 27th Street, 10 Floor
New York, NY 10001

Phone: 212-674-9145
Fax: 212-674-6506
Contact: Marie-Claire Picher

Office Hours: Variable
Staff: Volunteer
Geographic Scope: City-wide

Organizational Focus:
Interactive theater workshops for
social change. The laboratory uses
Augusto Boal's approach to theater
for analyzing problems and inventing
new ways of confronting oppression.

General Description:
Techniques explore relations of
power and group solutions to
concrete problems through living
body imagery. Spectators propose
alternative solutions to given
situations by coming directly into the
playing area and acting. Programs
include on-site workshops and
intensive trainings for educators,
human service and (mental) health
workers.

Multi-lingual: Spanish, French and
Italian

Organizational Resources: Workshop
Facilitators

Issues:
Education
Arts/Culture
Social Justice
Human Rights

THIRD WORLD NEWSREEL

335 West 38th Street, 5th Fl.
New York, NY 10018

Phone: 212-947-9277
Fax: 212-594-6417
Contact: Kenyatta Tyehimba, Office
           Manager

Office Hours: Mon.-Fri. 10am-6pm
Staff: Paid and volunteer

Organizational Focus:
Media and representation.

General Description:
Third World Newsreel distributes &
produces videos and films that seek
to represent and empower people of
color and are from the perspective of
those artists from these
communities. Newsreel also has
training workshops in film and video
production to train up-and-coming
artists in representing their concerns
and empowering their communities
through media.
Membership Organization?: No

Issues: Constituencies:
Arts/Culture   Multi-Racial
Anti-Racism
Media
Social Justice
Human Rights

THORPE FAMILY RESIDENCE

2252 Crotona Ave.
Bronx, NY 10457

Phone: 718-933-7312
Fax: 718-933-7311
Contact: Sister B. Lenniger, Exec.
            Director

Office?: Yes
Staff: Paid and volunteer
Geographic Scope: Crotona, Bronx

Organizational Focus:
Temporary housing with services for homeless mothers and children.

General Description:
To enable women to live independently in permanent housing; finish school; maintain a job. We provide education and awareness of public policy.

Multi-lingual: Spanish, French & Creole

Organizational Resources:
Newsletter, flyers, and facilitators.
Membership Organization?: No

Issues:	Constituencies:
Housing/	Homeless
Homelessness	mothers with
	children

TRANSPORTATION ALTERNATIVES

92 St. Marks Place
New York, NY 10009

Phone: 212-475-4600
Fax: 212-475-4551
Contact: Paul Harrison,
            Administrator

Office Hours: 10am-6pm
Staff: Paid
Geographic Scope: City-wide

Organizational Focus:
Transportation Alternatives (T.A.) advocates environmentally-sound transportation, including bicycling, walking, improved public transit, and reduced automobile use.

General Description:
T.A. is a 20-year old, 3,000-member grassroots organization whose goals include cleaner air, a more livable city, more equitable transportation systems, reduced energy use, lessening global warming trends, and protection and creation of open space.

Organizational Resources:
Newsletter, pamphlets, videos, speakers about transportation issues, technical and organizing skills.
Regular Public Meetings: Bimonthly
Membership Organization?: Yes
Membership Requirements: $20
Annual Dues

Issues:	Constituencies:
Environment	Multi-Racial
Civic	Bicyclists
	Pedestrians
	Transit Users

U.S./PUERTO RICO SOLIDARITY NETWORK

PO Box 350, Jerome Ave. Sta. Bronx, NY 10468

Phone: 718-601-4751
Fax: 718-601-3909
Contact: Rosa Garcia, Co-
          Coordinator

Office?:   No
Staff: None
Geographic Scope: City-wide

Organizational Focus:
Active support for independence and self-determination for Puerto Rico.

General Description:
We promote a working class perspective in our solidarity work and build ties between the workers' movement in the U.S. and Puerto Rico. We are developing a national network of Puerto Rico solidarity, open to all groups and individuals who share our goals.

Bi-lingual: Spanish

Organizational Resources: Newsletter, *Puerto Rico Update* (bilingual publication), workshops facilitators and speakers on any issue dealing with Puerto Rico, including Puerto Rican political prisoners.
Regular Public Meetings: 3-5 a year
Membership Organization?: Yes
Membership Requirements: Work for P.R's independence, attend meetings, and join a committee.

Issues: Constituencies:
Int'l Solidarity   Multi-Racial
Social Justice   Latino/Hispanic
Human Rights   Caribbean
Puerto Rico's Independence

US TIBET COMMITTEE

1 East 32nd Street
New York, NY 10016

Phone: 212-213-5011
Fax: 212-779-9245
E-Mail: ustcsft@igc.apc.org

Office Hours: 9am-6pm
Staff: Paid
Geographic Scope: City-wide

General Description:
USTC is an independent human rights organization which promotes public awareness of the Tibetan people's non violent struggle for human rights and self determination.

Multi-lingual: Tibetan and Hindi

Organizational Resources: Newsletter, pamphlets, videos, and speakers.
Membership Organization?:Yes
Membership Requirements: $25 annual membership

Issues:
Human Rights
Peace/Anti-Militarism
Environment
Social Justice
Reproductive Rights

UNITED TIL COALITION OF HARLEM

1878 7th Ave. Suite 1
New York, NY 10026

Phone: 212-663-3710
Fax: 212-283-2194
Contact: Jackie Wilson, President

Office Hours: Mon-Thurs.10am-2pm
Staff: Volunteer
Geographic Scope: Central and West Harlem

Organizational Focus:
The focus of United TIL Coalition of Harlem is to monitor, observe and improve the affordable housing stock in Harlem.

General Description:
The Coalition assists tenants in taking over the management and eventual ownership of buildings now owned and managed by the City of New York HPD. The coalition educates and empowers tenants who live in privately owned buildings which show signs of abandonment.

Organizational Resources: Pamphlets
Regular Public Meetings: Quarterly
Membership Organization?: No

Issues:	Constituencies:
Tenant Advocacy	African American
Housing/	Caribbean
Homelessness	

UPPER ROOM AIDS MINISTRY, INC.

207 West 133rd Street
New York, NY 10030

Phone: 212-491-9000
Fax: 212-491-9069
Contact: Charles Taylor, Executive Assistant

Office Hours: Mon.-Fri. 9am-6pm
Staff: Paid and volunteer
Geographic Scope: Harlem +

Organizational Focus:
Provide physical and spiritual support to individuals and families who are affected by HIV/AIDS.

General Description:
"Adult Day Community Center," hot meals, spiritual guidance, case management, recreational activities, "scattered site housing" -- 60 family/individual housing units, full range of social services."

Bi-lingual: Spanish

Organizational Resources:
Newsletter
Membership Organization?: No

Issues:	Constituencies:
HIV/AIDS	HIV/AIDS
Housing/	affected
Homelessness	individuals
Health Care	

THE VALLEY INC.

1047 Amsterdam Avenue
New York, NY 10025

Phone: 212-222-2110
Fax: 212-222-4671
Contact: James Murray,
          Development Director

Office Hours: 9:00am-5:00pm
Staff: Paid and volunteer
Geographic Scope: City-wide

Organizational Focus:
Provide services to youth and
families: social services and
recreational programs.

General Description:
A multi-service youth agency whose
primary goal is to empower young
people (ages 14-24) to become
independent, self-sufficient and
responsible. Programs provided are
in the areas of education,
employment, recreation, creative
arts, counseling and leadership
development.

Bi-lingual: Spanish

Organizational Resources:
Newsletter, workshops, pamphlets,
referrals, conferences, and videos.
Regular Public Meetings: September-
June M,T,W,Th 5-7pm
Membership Organization?: No

Issues: Constituencies:
Youth   Youth
Education   Multi-Racial
Anti-Violence   Students
Anti-Racism
Health Care

VAMOS A LA PEÑA DEL BRONX

226 East 144th Street, 3rd Floor
Bronx, NY 10451

Phone: 718-402-9411
Contact: Nieves Ayress, Victor
          Toro, Co-Directors
Office Hours: 10am-10pm
Staff: Volunteer
Geographic Scope: South Bronx

Organizational Focus:
Multi-cultural community-based
programs including classes in art,
English, citizenship, sports; organizing
against domestic violence and
homelessness.

General Description:
Provides a meeting place which
emphasizes and supports the folkloric
arts of the communities we serve, as
well as provides information on and
organizes for housing, attaining legal
residency, and women's rights.

Multi-lingual: Spanish and Garífuna

Organizational Resources: Meeting
place; speakers.
Regular Public Meetings: Every three
months.
Membership Organization?: No

Issues: Constituencies:
Anti-Racism   Multi-Racial
Anti-Violence   Lesbians/Gays
Culture/Arts   Seniors
Education   Youth
Women's Rights   Women
Domestic Violence
Social Justice
Immigrants' Rights

VIDEOTECA DEL SUR

84 East 3rd Street, #5A
New York, NY 10003

Phone: 212-334-5257
Fax: 212-674-5405
Contact: Pedro Zurita, Exec. Dir.

Office Hours: Mon.-Fri. 9am-5pm
Staff: Paid and volunteer
Geographic Scope: City-wide

Organizational Focus: Dissemination
and exhibition of alternative Latin
American and Caribbean videos.

Multi-lingual: Spanish & Portuguese

Organizational Resources: Speakers
bureau on Latin American film and
video; can curate special events and
film and video festivals.

Issues:	Constituencies:
Arts/Culture	Latino/Hispanic
Education	Caribbean
Social Justice	Multi-Racial
	Native Latin
	American

VIETNAM VETERANS AGAINST THE WAR

PO Box 74 Van Brunt Station
Brooklyn, NY 11215

Phone: 718-826-1789
E-Mail: VVAW@buythe.org
Contact: Ben Chitty, Co-
Coordinator

Office?: No
Staff: None
Geographic Scope: City-wide

Organizational Focus:
Peace and social justice.

General Description:
Membership mainly Vietnam
veterans. Meet to discuss social
issues and plan participation in
movement activities. Not affiliated
with any political organization.

Organizational Resources:
Speakers' bureau, military counseling,
our newsletter *DMZ* is published 4-6
issues/year.
Regular Public Meetings: 2nd
Tuesday of month
Membership Organization?: Yes
Membership Requirements: Agree
with goals

Issues:	Constituencies:
Social Justice	Veterans
Peace/Anti-Militarism	

VIOLENCE INTERVENTION PROGRAM

PO Box 136, Triborough Station
New York, NY 10035

Phone: 212-360-5090
Fax: 212-410-9117
Contact: Grace Perez, Exec. Dir.

Office Hours: Mon.-Fri. 9am-5pm
Staff: Paid
Geographic Scope: East Harlem

Organizational Focus:
Bilingual/bicultural community-based domestic violence program addressing the plight of Latina battered women.

General Description:
Providing crisis intervention, long and short term empowerment counseling, legal information, referrals, advocacy, accompaniment, hotline and safe space to battered women of the East Harlem community, as well as to Spanish-speaking only and undocumented battered women living in NYC.

Bi-lingual: Spanish

Organizational Resources: Hotline
Membership Organization?: No

Issues: Constituencies:
Anti-Violence   Women
Domestic Violence   Latino/
Women's Rights   Hispanic

VISTAS LATINAS

c/o Miriam Hernandez
119 East 101 St. #4W
New York, NY 10029

Contact: Miriam Hernandez
Office: No
Staff: None
Geographic Scope: City-wide and national

Organizational Focus:
Vistas Latinas is an organization of Latina artists striving for better representation and visibility for Latina art and artists.

General Description:
Our mission is to disseminate information about Latina artists; to increase the number of exhibiting Latina artists; to develop organization and leadership among Latina artists; to build a broader Latina coalition for arts advocacy.

Bi-lingual: Spanish

Membership Organization?:Yes
Membership Requirement: Latina artists practicing visual arts

Issues: Constituencies:
Arts/Culture   Latino/Hispanic
                     Women

WAR RESISTERS LEAGUE (WRL)

339 Lafayette Street
New York, NY 10012

Phone: 212-228-0450
Fax: 212-228-6193
Contact: Ruth Benn, Director,
            National Office

Office Hours: Mon.-Fri. 9am-5pm
Staff: Paid and volunteer
Geographic Scope: City-wide and national

Organizational Focus:
Promoting pacifism and anti-war activities; striving nonviolently for the removal of all causes of war.

General Description:
WRL is a 70-year old pacifist, anti-war organization. Both our national office and a separate NYC local group can be found at the address above. Our newest program is children, youth, militarism & nonviolence.

Organizational Resources:
Newsletter, organizing manual and pamphlets, video on counter-recruitment, war tax resistance, books on nonviolence, pacifism, and international issues.
Membership Organization?: Yes
Membership Requirements:
Committed to non-violence

Issues:
Peace/Anti-Militarism
Anti-Violence

WBAI PACIFICA RADIO

505 8th Avenue
New York, NY 10018

Phone: 212-279-0707
Fax: 212-564-5359
Contact: Mario Murillo, Public
            Affairs Director

Office Hours: 9am-7pm
Staff: Paid and volunteer
Geographic Scope: City-wide

Organizational Focus:
WBAI is a non-commercial, listener-sponsored community radio station broadcasting to the New York metropolitan area.

General Description:
As a primarily volunteer broadcasting outlet, the station provides a space for the community to train and produce radio programs, and to keep the broader audience abreast of the political, social and cultural realities of the city, state and world.

Bi-lingual: Some programming in Spanish

Organizational Resources: We publish a program guide *Folio* 6 times a year; make public service announcements on the air; and WBAI staff and producers are available for public speaking.
Regular Public Meetings?: Yes
Membership Organization?: Yes
Membership Requirements: $50 annual fee for regular membership; $25 for students and seniors.

Issues:
Media

WEST HARLEM ENVIRONMENTAL ACTION (WHE ACT)

271 West 125th Street, Suite 211
New York, NY 10027

Phone: 212-961-1000
Fax: 212-961-1015
Contact: Peggy Shepard, Exec. Dir.

Office Hours: 9am-5pm
Staff: Paid
Geographic Scope: West Harlem and upper Manhattan

Organizational Focus:
Environmental justice and environmental racism.

General Description:
WheAct informs, educates and mobilizes community residents on quality of life issues like: air and water pollution, development, zoning and siting, health risks, environmental impact, toxics, waterfront devlopment, open space, and preservation. WheAct builds its advocacy base through outreach to neighborhood groups and religious, educational and medical institutions.

Organizational Resources:
Speakers' Bureau, Earth Crew youth group, hotline on sanitation and recycling issues.
Membership Organization?: Yes
Membership Requirements:
Neighborhood resident

Issues: Constituencies:
Environment   Multi-Racial
Gov't Accountability   African American
                       Latino/Hispanic

WESTSIDE SENIORS FOR ACTION (WSA)

140 West 105 Street, Suite 141
New York, NY 10025

Phone: 212-932-1200
Contact: Fred Gimino, Chairperson

Office Hours: 10am-5pm
Staff: Paid
Geographic Scope: Manhattan/
Upper Westside

Organizational Focus:
Better quality of life for seniors. WSA is concerned with all major issues relating to older people.

General Description:
A 17-year old grassroots, multi-ethnic organization. WSA has functioned as an effective advocacy group. Through education, dissemination of information, encouragement of self-advocacy, outreach, intergenerational program, it works for the elderly.

Bi-lingual: Spanish

Regular Public Meetings: Once a month
Membership Organization?: Yes
Membership Requirements:
Interested senior citizens

Issues: Constituencies:
Senior   Seniors
Advocacy
Quality of life

WETLANDS RAINFOREST ACTION GROUP (W.R.A.G.)

c/o Wetlands Preserve
161 Hudson Street
New York, NY 10013

Phone: 212-966-5244
Fax: 212-925-8715
Contact: James Hansen, Dir.

Office Hours: 12-7pm
Staff: Paid
Geographic Scope: City-wide

Organizational Focus:
Educate citizens of the greater New York area about threats to tropical forests and indigenous peoples.

General Description:
W.R.A.G. holds monthly meetings that address a wide range of issues including rainforests and indigenous peoples. We hold regular demonstrations to press for corporate accountability and social justice.

Organizational Resources: Videos, speakers, research materials
Regular Public Meetings: 1st Tuesday of each month
Membership Organization?: No

Issues: Constituencies:
Environment   Multi-Racial
Corporate and
Gov't Accountability
Human Rights
Social Justice

WOMEN AND AIDS RESOURCE NETWORK (WARN)

30 Third Avenue, Suite 212
Brooklyn, NY 11217

Phone: 718-596-6007
Fax: 718-596-6041
Contact: Yvonne Chambers, Exec. Director

Office Hours: 9am-8pm
Staff: Paid
Geographic Scope: City-wide

Organizational Focus:
The mission of WARN is to empower and improve the quality of life for women and their families who are affected and infected by HIV/AIDS.

General Description:
WARN currently offers advocacy, case management services, counseling, supportive scattered-site housing, outreach, education services, recreational services.

Multi-lingual: Spanish, French,Creole

Organizational Resources:
Pamphlets and workshops.
Membership Organization?: No

Issues: Constituencies:
HIV/AIDS   Women
Health Care   Lesbian/Gay
Women's Right   Multi-Racial
Lesbian/Gay   Youth

WOMEN FIGHTING POVERTY CONFERENCE

c/o M. Murphy
Fed. of Protestant Welfare Agencies
281 Park Avenue South
New York, NY 10010

Phone: 212-477-3889
Contact: Miriam Friedlander

Organizational Focus:
To call attention to the problems of women fighting poverty, and to stimulate advocacy for just and equitable solutions that are grounded in a first-hand understanding of women's lives and needs.

General Description:
This is a diverse ad-hoc coalition of about 40 women's organizations, service, labor and advocacy groups. Through an annual conference and other forums, networking and information-sharing we seek to develop a voice in the formation of government policies that affect them.

Bi-lingual: Spanish

Organizational Resources: An annual conference and other forums; written reports of the conferences.
Regular Public Meetings: Each spring
Membership Organization?: No

Issues:	Constituencies:
Women's Rights	Women
Gov't Accountability	Multi-Racial
Health Care	Seniors
Anti-Violence	Youth
Social Justice	

WOMEN FOR RACIAL & ECONOMIC EQUALITY (WREE)

198 Broadway, #606
New York, NY 10038

Phone: 212-385-1103
Contact: Ismay Harrigan, NY
           Director

Office?:   Yes
Staff: Paid and volunteer
Geographic Scope: City-wide and national

Organizational Focus:
One of the early progressive women's organizations in the 70's focused on the concerns of working women and women of color. WREE seeks to bring these issues to the attention of the mainstream women's movement in the United States.

General Description:
A multi-racial organization focusing on race and class issues too often neglected by the mainstream women's movement.

Bi-lingual: Spanish

Organizational Resources:
Newsletter, speakers, workshop facilitators, and forums.
Regular Public Meetings: Sept.-May
Membership Organization?: Yes
Membership Requirements: Sliding scale annual dues based on income.

Issues:	Constituencies:
Women's Rights	Women
Anti-Racism	Multi-Racial
Health Care	
Econ. Development	
Workers' Rights	

WOMEN MAKE MOVIES

462 Broadway, 5th Floor
New York, NY 10013

Phone: 212-925-0606
Fax: 212-925-2052

Office Hours: Mon.-Fri. 10am-6pm
Staff: Paid and volunteer
Geographic Scope: City-wide

Organizational Focus:
To facilitate the development of
feminist media through programs for
both users and makers of
independent film and video.

General Description:
We are a multi-cultural distribution
service and resource center
providing fiscal sponsorship,
workshops, seminars, screenings and
a database for women of color. Also,
WMM distributes over 350
multicultural films and videotapes by
and about women to community,
educational, and cultural groups.

Organizational Resources: Media
resource center, pamphlets, videos
(with screening room), meeting
rooms, workshops and seminars.
Membership Organization?:Yes
Membership Requirements: A tax-
deductible contribution

Issues: Constituencies:
Media   Women
Women's Rights   Multi-Racial
Arts/Culture   Lesbian/Gay
Education   Multi-Cultural
Lesbian/Gay

WOMEN PLAYWRIGHTS COLLECTIVE

Phone: 718-885-1119
Contact: Nancy Dean, Founding
            Member

Office?:   No
Staff: None
Geographic Scope: City-wide

Organizational Focus: Developing the
work of lesbian playwrights.

General Description:
The collective supports strong,
compelling work from a lesbian
perspective. Believing that good plays
are truth tellers and powerful agents
for social awareness and social
change. At our 2-3 meetings a
month, we hear one another's work,
offer constructive criticism, and when
our players are ready we consider
arranging for production.

Organizational Resources:
The collective presents productions
once or twice a year.
Regular Public Meetings: 1st & 3rd
Wednesdays of month
Membership Organization?: Yes
Membership Requirements: All
lesbian playwrights.

Issues: Constituencies:
Arts/Culture   Women
Lesbian/Gay   Lesbian/Gay
Social Justice

WOMENCARE

322 Eighth Avenue, Suite 1700
New York, NY 100

Phone: 212-463-9500
Fax: 212-463-0477
Contact: Eileen Hogan, Exec. Dir.

Office Hours: 9am-5pm
Staff: Paid and volunteer
Geographic Scope: City-wide

Organizational Focus:
WomenCare is an
advocacy/mentorship program for
mothers coming out of prison.

General Description:
WomenCare provides the mothers
with the unique opportunity to
develop a relationship with a
volunteer mentor based on trust
which will ultimately lead to
successful transition into the
community.

Bi-lingual: Spanish

Organizational Resources: Speakers,
pamphlets, training to become a
volunteer mentor
Regular Public Meetings: First
Tuesday of each month, call to verify.
Membership Organization?: No

Issues: Constituencies:
Crime/   Women
Criminal Justice   Youth
HIV/AIDS   Multi-racial
Welfare Advocacy   Lesbian/Gay
Social Justice

WOMEN'S ACTION ALLIANCE

370 Lexington Ave, Suite 603
New York, NY 10017

Phone: 212-532-8330
Fax: 212-779-2846
Contact: Karel R. Amaranth, Exec.
           Director

Office Hours: Mon-Fri 9:30-5:30pm
Staff: Paid and volunteer
Geographic Scope: National

Organizational Focus:
Self-determination for all women

General Description:
We create, test, and implement
innovative, multicultural program
models through community-based
organizations to effect positive
change in the lives of women and
girls. We provide training and
technical assistance in the areas of
self esteem, equity in education and
in the workplace and health.

Bi-lingual: Spanish

Organizational Resources:
Newsletter, pamphlets, videos,
meeting space, speakers, resource
center, information and referral
service, library, publications,
internship/volunteer program, career
services.
Membership Organization?: Yes
Membership Requirements: Annual
fee

Issues: Constituencies:
Women's Rights   Women
                       Economically-
                       Disadvantaged
                       Youth

WOMEN'S HEALTH ACTION MOBILIZATION (WHAM!)

PO Box 733
New York, NY 10009

Phone: 212-560-7177
Contact: Dina Levy
Office?: No
Staff: None
Geographic Scope: City-wide

Organizational Focus:
Women's and other human health issues.

General Description:
WHAM! Holds weekly meetings that help to keep women activists informed about organizing opportunities. We participate in coalitions as well as organize our own demonstrations and actions to protect full reproductive health care for all women.

Regular Public Meetings: 7pm Wed.
Membership Organization?: No

Issues:
Health Care
Reproductive Rights
Women's Rights

WOMEN'S HEALTH EDUCATION PROJECT

2271 Second Avenue
New York, NY 10035

Phone: 212-987-0066
Fax: 212-987-3278
Contact: Cynthia Williams, Program Director

Office Hours: Mon.-Fri. 9am-5pm
Staff: Paid
Geographic Scope: City-wide

Organizational Focus:
Women's health education

General Description:
Women's Health Education Project is dedicated to encouraging and facilitating the self-empowerment of women through alternative and holistic health education, resource sharing and information exchange. Our programs are offered as part of a community, inclusive of race, class, ethnicity, sexuality, ability and age.

Bi-lingual: Spanish

Organizational Resources:
Newsletter, telephone referral service for a wide range of women's health concerns, resource guides to women's health facilities in NYC: abortion, childbirth and gyn.
Membership Organization?: No

Issues: Constituencies:
Health Care Women
Women's Rights
Housing/Homelessness

WOMEN'S PRISON ASSOCIATION & HOME, INC. (WPA)

110 Second Avenue
New York, NY 10003

Phone: 212-674-1163
Fax: 212-677-1981
Contact: Ann Jacobs, Exec. Dir.

Office Hours: Mon.-Fri. 9am-6pm
Staff: Paid
Geographic Scope: Lower East Side

Organizational Focus:
WPA is a nonprofit agency working
to create opportunities for change in
the lives of women prisoners, ex-
prisoners, and their families.

General Description:
WPA provides alternative to incarceration, residential and transitional
services programs enabling women
to acquire skills necessary to end
their criminal justice involvement and
make positive, healthy choices for
themselves and their families. WPA
maintains a tradition of advocacy
designed to promote community-
based responses to crime.

Bi-lingual: Spanish

Organizational Resources: Foster
care handbook.
Membership Organization?: No

Issues:	Constituencies:
Crime/	Women
Criminal Justice	Multi-Racial
HIV/AIDS	Children of
Housing/	Criminal justice
Homelessness	involved women

WOMEN'S RESOURCE CENTER OF NEW YORK, INC.

2315 Broadway, 4th Fl.
New York, NY 10024

Phone: 212-875-8533
Fax: 212-875-8629
Contact: Deborah Carlow, Dir.

Office Hours: Mon.-Fri. 9am-5pm
Staff: Paid and volunteer
Geographic Scope: City-wide

Organizational Focus:
To provide information, referrals,
resources to women and
organizations that serve women.

General Description:
The Women's Resource Center is a
unique clearinghouse of information
that connects women, at no cost, to
thousands of organizations and
resources. Basic use of the center is
free while membership offers
additional services including a newsletter, calendar of events, and more.

Bi-lingual: Spanish

Organizational Resources:
Newsletter, database, resource
library, topic files, women-owned
business files, and a speakers' bureau.
Membership Organization?: Yes

Issues:	Constituencies:
Women's Rights	Women
Health	
Finance	
Legal	
Education	
Parenting	
Social Services	

WORLDWIDE, LTD.

29 King Street, Suite 31
New York, NY 10014

Phone: 212-924-7929
Fax: Same
Contact: Lisa Beaudoin, Special
            Projects Coordinator

Office Hours: 9am-6pm
Staff: Volunteer
Geographic Scope: City-wide

Organizational Focus:
Worldview assists educators in
linking social justice, economic and
environmental issues.

General Description:
Worldview assists with curriculum
development and research on a
variety of issues; maintains a resource
center; conducts teacher workshops;
and provides educational
presentations.

Organizational Resources: In addition
to our resource center, we have
environmental videos available.
Regular Public Meetings?: No
Membership Organization?: No

Issues:	Constituencies:
Environment	Multi-Racial
Int'l Trade	
Corporations	
Social Justice	
Human Rights	
Economic Development	
Student	
Int'l Solidarity	

YOUTH ACTION PROGRAM

1280 Fifth Avenue
New York, NY 10029

Phone: 212-860-8170
Fax: 212-860-8894
Contact: Sonia Bu, Exec. Director

Office Hours: Mon.-Fri. 9am-5pm
Staff: Paid
Geographic Scope: East Harlem

Organizational Focus:
Education, community development
and urban renewal; developing
leadership skills and self-
empowerment in youth.

General Description:
Youth Action is a non-profit
educational organization committed
to youth leadership development and
community building in East Harlem.
Our programs are designed to instill
in young people a sense of self-
worth, pride and awareness of one's
culture and ethnic heritage.

Bi-lingual: Spanish

Regular Public Meetings: No
Membership Organization?: No

Issues:	Constituencies:
Youth	Youth
Community Dev.	African American
Education	Latino/Hispanic
Housing/Homelessness	

YOUTH AGAINST RACISM AND POVERTY (YARP)

144 North 9th Street #31
Brooklyn, NY 11211

Phone: 718-963-2518
          800-655-Yarp
Fax: 718-956-7748
Contact: Ben-Hur Uribe,
          Coordinator

Office?:   No
Staff: Volunteer
Geographic Scope: City-wide

Organizational Focus:
High school, college and working
youth.

General Description:
We fight for the rights of young
people on the program of a
guaranteed job, free education at all
levels, and to double the minimum
wage. We organize in our schools,
work places and communities. We
call rallies and demonstrations as a
method of struggle to improve our
lives and challenge the powers-that-
be that consider young people to be
useless and a nuisance.

Bi-lingual: Spanish

Organizational Resources: Speakers,
leaflets and organizers.
Membership Organization?: Yes

Issues:	Constituencies:
Youth	Youth
Education	
Anti-Racism	
Social Justice	
Int'l Solidarity	

YOUTH AGENDA

300 West 43rd Street, 3rd Floor
New York, NY 10036

Phone: 212-977-5455
Contact: Keith Hyman

Office Hours: 10am-6pm
Staff: Volunteer
Geographic Scope: City-wide

Organizational Focus:
Youth Agenda is a coalition of young
people, youth workers, teachers and
community activists.

General Description:
Since its formation in 1994, Youth
Agenda has organized rallies, press
conferences legislative visits and vigils
to pressure elected officials to create
policies that support youth and
families. A broad-based coalition,
Youth Agenda represents over 120
organizations and many individuals.

Multi-lingual: Creole, Spanish,
Korean, Chinese

Organizational Resources: Newsletter and training in lobbying, understanding city and state government,
and meeting space. Youth Agenda
also provides a youth voice and vision
to other coalitions.
Membership Organization?: Yes
Membership Requirements: Youth,
youth service agencies and corpor-
ations, organizations and individuals
who consider the welfare of the
City's youth as their responsibility.

Issues:	Constituencies:
Students	Multi-Racial
Social Justice	Youth
Voting Rights	Multi-ethnic/
	religious

YOUTH COMMUNICATION

144 West 27th Street, 8 R
New York, NY 10001

Phone: 212-242-3270
Fax: 212-242-7057
Contact: Keith Hefner, Exec. Dir.

Office Hours: 8:30am-6pm
Staff: Paid and volunteer
Geographic Scope: City-wide

Organizational Focus:
Making teen voices heard by
publishing two citywide magazines
written by youth for an audience of
their peers.

General Description:
Y.C. trains teens in journalism and
publishes New Youth Connections
and Foster Care Youth United with a
readership of 200,000 teens. We
also train educators and community
activists to work with young people
on their writing.

Multi-lingual: Spanish, Cantonese

Organizational Resources: Newsletter and magazines available by
subscription.
Membership Organization?: No

Issues: Constituencies:
Media   Multi-Racial
Youth   Youth

YOUTH FORCE, INC.

300 West 43rd St., 3rd Floor
New York, NY 10036

Contact: Henry Diaz, Youth
Organizer

Office Hours: 10am-9pm
Staff: Paid and volunteer
Geographic Scope: City-wide

Organizational Focus:
Youth Force was created by young
people to alert other youth to the
fact that we are not powerless, we
should be seen and heard. We have the
ability and right to act for change.

General Description:
Youth Force supports young people
throughout the city to initiate actions
that improve schools or neighborhoods; reaches out to help other
youth change public policies; and
provides a youth voice wherever it is
absent.

Multi-lingual: Spanish and Korean

Organizational Resources: Videos,
publications produced by youth,
training for youth and adults, history
of social change movements, peer
counseling, street outreach, etc.
Regular Public Meetings: Often, call
for schedule
Membership Organization?: Yes
Membership Requirements: All
youth in NYC who are committed to
building a better city.

Issues: Constituencies:
Community   Multi-Racial
organizing   Youth
Leadership   Juvenile
development   Delinquents
Student   Youth
Social Justice

YOUTH UPRISING

Box One, 300 W. 43rd St., 3rd Fl
New York, NY 10036

Contact: Song Park

Office Hours: None
Geographic Scope: City-wide

Organizational Focus:
Youth Uprising was founded when
young people discovered they did
have a public/independent voice while
representing their youth programs.

General Description:
Youth Uprising has sponsored
campaigns to restructure the NY
Police Department, to improve the
representation of youth in NYC's
media, and unite youth from
Germany and NY together through
an exchange program to look at
issues like xenophobia. Youth
Uprising is a leading force in the
mobilization of Youth Agenda.

Multi-lingual: Spanish and Korean

Organizational Resources: Can
provide trainings in civil disobedience
and link youth to lawyers and
experienced activists to support their
organizing.
Membership Organization?: Yes, All
"radi-cool" youth who have a mind of
their own, the courage to change
things, and the heart to make sure
those changes are for the better.

Issues:	Constituencies:
Youth	Multi-racial/
Social Justice	religious/
Human Rights	sexual
	orientation/
	gender

Part 2:

AGENCIA INTERNACIONAL PARA ASUNTOS DE ARTISTAS PERTENECIENTES A MINORIAS

ACP, Jr. State Office Building
163 W. 125 Street, Suite 909
New York, NY 10027

Teléfono: 212-749-5298
Fax: 212-749-3745
Contacto: Gregory Mills, Chair
Horario: Lunes-viernes, 9-5pm
Personal: Asalariado y voluntario
Area Geográfica: Toda la ciudad

Foco de la Organización:
Facilitar recursos, instrucción y
visibilidad a artistas de color

Descripción General:
Se encarga de la galería del edificio de
oficinas del Estado; publica *Uptown
News*, patrocinan una conferencia
anual sobre el estado de las artes,
ofrece instrucción a artistas y
organizaciones sobre administración
en lo no lucrativo, ofrece festivales
de cine y seminarios.

Recursos: Boletín, conferenciantes,
talleres, conferencias, local de
reuniones, consultatores.
Organización de miembros: Sí
Requisitos: Ser un artista de color o
trabajar con una organización cultural que sirva comunidades de color

Temas: Población Servida:
Artes y cultura   Mujeres
Educación   Multiracial
VIH/SIDA   Tercera edad
Responsabilidad del gobierno
Medios de comunicación

ALIANZA DE NUEVA YORK PARA LA JUSTICIA AMBIENTAL

271 West 125th Street, 303
New York, NY 10027

Teléfono: 212-866-4120
Fax: 212-866-4511
Contacto: Michelle DePass, Dir.
Horario: 9am-5pm
Personal: Asalariado y voluntario
Area Geográfica: Toda la ciudad

Foco de la Organización:
Asegurar un ambiente que sustente la
salud humana, la protección
ambiental justa y la participación
abierta en la política del medio
ambiente.

Descripción General:
La Alianza une a organizaciones de base
que se preocupan por asegurar el
derecho de las comunidades de color y
de bajos ingresos a un medio ambiente
limpio y seguro. La Alianza trabaja para
lograr sus objetivos apoyando la
educación y la participación, facilitando
la creación de una red que unifique la
ciudad de Nueva York, organizando
eventos y foros y funcionando como un
centro de información.

Recursos: Boletín, referencias de
conferenciantes, folletos, recursos
técnicos y legales.
Reuniones: Cada dos meses
Organización de Miembros: Sí
Requisitos: Apoyar nuestros
objetivos.

Temas: Población Servida:
Medio ambiente   Gentes de color
Justicia social   Barrios de bajos
Transporte   ingresos

ALIANZA DOMINICANA, INC.

2410 Amsterdam Ave. 4th Fl.
New York, NY 10033

Teléfono: 212-740-1960
Fax: 212-740-1967
Contacto: Marianela Nuñez,
              Directora del
              Programa
Horario: 9:00am-5:00pm
Personal: Asalariado
Area Geográfica: Washington
Heights-Manhattan

Foco de la Organización:
Ayudar a los niños, jóvenes y familias
a romper el ciclo vicioso de la
pobreza y lograr su mayor potencial
como miembros de la comunidad.

Descripción General:
Tenemos muchos programas
incluyendo: el único programa de
tratamiento para la adicción de cocaína
y crack en Washington Heights y el
único que está localizado en una
organización comunitaria; un programa
de servicio para personas VIH positivas;
una clínica de salud mental; un proyecto
de ciudadanía; un proyecto de salud e
inmunización; un programa de
orientación y entrenamiento juvenil y
un centro recreativo comunitario.

Recursos: Boletín, folletos, servicios y
programas.
Reuniones: Sí

Temas: Población Servida:
Rehabilitación   Latinos/Hispanos
de drogas
Vivienda
Educación
Derechos humanos
Derechos económicos

AMANAKA'A AMAZON NETWORK

584 Broadway, Room 814
New York, NY 10012

Teléfono: 212-925-5299
Fax: 212-925-7743
Contacto: Zezé Weiss,
              Presidente
Horario: 10am-6pm
Personal: Asalariado y voluntario
Area Geográfica: Toda la ciudad

Foco de la Organización:
La selva amazónica y sus pueblos.

Descripción General:
Dedicada a la educación del público
norteamericano en cuanto a la selva
amazónica y sus pueblos.

Multilingüe: inglés, portugués y
francés

Recursos: Boletín, videos,
facilitadores de talleres, local de
reuniones.
Organización de Miembros: Sí
Reuniones: Semana Amazónica cada
primavera
Requisitos: $25 o $35 por dos años

Temas: Población Servida:
Educación   Pueblos del
Medio ambiente   Amazonas
Derechos humanos

ASOCIACION DE INQUILINOS INGERSOLL, INC.

173 Myrtle Avenue, Grd. Fl.
Brooklyn, NY 11201

Teléfono: 718-875-6043
Fax: 718-858-5249
Contacto: Michael E. Boyd,
Director Ejecutivo
Horario: Lunes-Viernes 9am-
5pm, Sábados 10-2pm
Personal: Asalariado y voluntario
Area Geográfica: Toda la ciudad

Foco de la Organización:
Servicio y acción social

Descripción General:
Centro de servicios varios, no
lucrativo y con base en la comunidad,
con programas para jóvenes,
adolescentes y personas mayores.
Los programas van desde un club de
fotografía, artes marciales y danza,
biblioteca juvenil, programas de
recuperación, hasta información y
recomendaciones.

Recursos: Información sobre
VIH/SIDA, mediación juvenil,
seminarios, intercambio de
conferenciantes sobre temas sociales
Reuniones: Ultimo lunes del mes
Organización de miembros: Sí
Requisitos: Residentes de Ingersoll

Temas:	Población Servida:
Justicia social	Multiracial
Igualdad económica	

ASOCIACION Y HOGAR PARA MUJERES ENCARCELADAS (WPA)

110 Second Avenue
New York, NY 10003

Teléfono: 212-674-1163
Fax: 212-677-1981
Contacto: Ann Jacobs, Directora
Ejecutiva
Horario: Lunes a viernes 9-6pm
Personal: Asalariado
Area Geográfica: Lower East Side

Foco de la Organización:
WPA es una agencia con fines no
lucrativos que se ocupa de crear
oportunidades para el cambio en las
vidas de mujeres encarceladas,
excarcelarias, y sus familias.

Descripción General:
WPA proporciona alternativas a la
encarcelación, servicios de vivienda y
programas de transición que
permiten a las mujeres adquirir los
conocimientos necesarios para
terminar su relación con el sistema
penal y para elegir opciones positivas
y sanas para ellas y sus familias. WPA
ha abogado tradicionalmente por
promover respuestas al crimen
basadas en la acción comunitaria.

Recursos: Manual sobre foster care
Organización de miembros: No

Temas:	Población Servida:
Crimen	Mujeres
Justicia criminal	Multiracial
VIH/SIDA	Hijos de mujeres
Vivienda	relacionadas con el
	sistema penal

CAPITULO DE NUEVA YORK DEL CONGRESO NACIONAL PARA LOS DERECHOS DE PUERTO RICO

PO Box 205-098, Sunset Sta.
Brooklyn, NY 11220

Teléfono: 718-388-8056
Fax: 718-788-4986
Contacto: Annette Hernández
Oficina: No
Personal: Voluntario
Area Geográfica: Toda la ciudad

Descripción General:
Desde 1981 el Congreso Nacional para los Derechos de Puerto Rico ha trabajado por el fortalecimiento de la comunidad. Sus actividades incluyen foros educativos, defensa y apoyo de una conciencia política común entre los latinos y en particular en la comunidad puertorriqueña.

Recursos: Boletín, *Latino Issues Update,* conferenciantes
Reuniones: Foros en mayo y octubre
Organización de miembros: Sí
Requisitos: $15 de cuota anual

Temas: Población Servida:
Antiracismo   Medio ambiente
Justicia social   Latina/Hispana
Juventud   Multiracial

CAUCUS DE MUJERES DOMINICANAS

P.O. Box 5602, Manhattanville Sta
New York, NY 10027

Teléfono: 212-315-2580 o
                718-882-2921
Contacto: Zenaida Mendez o
                Genara Necos
Personal: Voluntario
Area Geográfica: Toda la ciudad

Foco de la Organización:
Unir a las mujeres dominicanas en Nueva York con el propósito de identificar los problemas que les afectan.

Descripción General:
El Caucus promueve actividades sociales, políticas, educativas y culturales que ayudan al desarrollo de la mujer. Se relaciona con organizaciones similares para combatir practicas y actitudes negativas que afectan a la mujer y apoyan la lucha de la mujer latinoamericana en general.

Recursos: Conferenciantes sobre asuntos de la comunidad, toma de poder político y otros asuntos que afectan a la mujer en particular. Talleres sobre cancer del seno, encuentro juvenil, día internacional de la mujer y seminarios.
Reuniones: El primer sábado del mes
Organización de Miembros: Sí
Requisitos: Cuota mensual opcional

Temas: Población Servida:
Antiviolencia   Latinos
Derechos   Multiétnica
de la mujer y del inmigrante
Toma de poder económico

CENTRO DE SERVICIOS PARA LAS COMUNIDADES LESBIANA Y GAY

208 West 13th Street
New York, NY 10011

Teléfono:	212-620-7310
Fax:	212-924-2657
Contacto:	Richard Burns, Director Ejecutivo
Horario:	9am-11pm
Personal:	Asalariado y voluntario

Area Geográfica: Toda la ciudad

Foco de la Organización: Comunidad lesbiana y gay, con énfasis en facilitar la organización comunitaria.

Descripción General:
Proporciona programas sobre salud, servicio social, recreo, educación, y cultura a la comunidad lesbiana y gay.

Recursos: Local de reuniones, boletín, conferenciantes, salud, y otros programas de interés a jóvenes y adultos
Reuniones: Durante todo el año
Organización de miembros: No

Temas:	Población Servida:
Lesbiana/Gay	Las comunidades
VIH//SIDA	lesbiana y gay
Derechos Humanos	

CENTRO PARA LA ELIMINACION DE LA VIOLENCIA

PO Box 200279
Brooklyn, NY 11200

Teléfono:	718-439-4612
Fax:	718-439-0016
Contacto:	Judith Kahan, Directora Ejecutiva
Horario:	8 am-6pm
Personal:	Asalariado

Area Geográfica: Toda la ciudad

Foco de la Organización:
Dotar a sobrevivientes de violencia doméstica y sus niños con un medio ambiente sano y seguro.

Descripción General:
CEVFI patrocina 2 programas: un espacio para mujeres maltratadas y sus niños, un local para el desarrollo de los niños, y una guardería para los hijos de residentes.

Multilingüe: Criollo, Hindi, Punjabi

Recursos:
Tenemos una línea telefónica en operación 24 horas al día (intervenciones de emergencia, recomendaciones) y un grupo de apoyo fuera del local para no residentes. Las mujeres interesadas en un grupo de apoyo para mujeres maltratadas pueden llamar al 718-439-1000.
Organización de miembros: No

Temas:	Población Servida:
Anti-violencia	Multiracial
Vivienda	Mujeres
Derechos de	Juventud
las mujeres	

CENTRO PARA LA INDEPENDENCIA DE LOS MINUSVALIDOS EN NUEVA YORK

841 Broadway, 2nd Fl.
New York, NY 10003

Teléfono: 212-674-2300
Fax: 212-254-5953
Contacto: Marilyn Saviola,
             Directora Ejecutiva
Oficina: Sí
Personal: Asalariado
Area Geográfica: Manhattan

Foco de la Organización:
Integrar a los minusválidos en la comunidad.

Descripción General:
Abogacía de sistemas.

Multilingüe: ASL (Lenguage Americano por Señas), Español

Organización de miembros: No

Temas: Población Servida:
Derechos de   Minusválidos
los minuválidos
Salud
Vivienda
Derechos humanos

CENTRO PARA LOS DERECHOS DE LOS INMIGRANTES (CIR)

48 Saint Marks Place
New York, NY 10003

Teléfono: 212-505-6890
Fax: 212-995-5876
Contacto: Roseann Micallef, Dir.
Horario: Lunes-Viernes 9:30-5:30
Personal: Asalariado
Area Geográfica: Toda la ciudad

Foco de la Organización:
Proteger y aumentar los derechos de los inmigrantes sin importar su status legal.

Descripción General:
Los inmigrantes son asistidos a través de organizaciones comunales, educación, política pública, abogacía y servicios legales. CIR también ofrece información, referencias, consejería y abogacía sobre inmigración, empleo y beneficios públicos a través de su línea telefónica de lunes a jueves, 10:00 a 1:00 de la tarde en la extensión 129.

Multilingüe: francés, inglés, cantonés y mandarín.

Recursos: Hojas informativas sobre los derechos basados en las leyes de inmigración, empleo y beneficios públicos. También estamos disponibles para llevar a cabo adiestramientos para organizaciones comunales y talleres para el público inmigrante.
Requisitos: Cuota de $35.

Temas: Población Servida:
Derechos   Multiétnico
del inmigrante
Derechos humanos
Derechos de la mujer

CIRCLE OF SISTAHS

Schomburg Satellite Academy
1010 Rev. James A. Polite Ave.
Bronx, NY 11459

Teléfono: 718-542-2700
Fax: 718-875-3120
Contacto: Mara Benitez,
Coordinadora
Horario: Lunes-Viernes 8:30-3pm
Personal: Asalariado y voluntario
Area Geográfica: El sur del Bronx

Foco de la Organización:
Circle of Sistahs es un grupo de
mujeres jóvenes de color en el sur
del Bronx que trabajan juntas para 1)
explorar temas diversos 2) luchar
contra el sexismo y el racismo y 3)
sanarse a si mismas. Analizamos la
sociedad, creamos nuestras propias
celebraciones y ritos y nos adiestra-
mos a compartir nuestros conocimientos: cada una enseña a la otra.

Recursos: Facilitadores de talleres y
un libro de referencias para mujeres
(una revista colectiva de nuestras
ideas, sueños, poesias y más).
Tenemos muchos eventos culturales,
ferias sobre la salud y también
nuestra celebración del Día de la
Mujer esta abierta al público.
Organización de miembros: Sí
Requisitos: Abierto a todas las
mujeres jóvenes de color.

Temas:
Derechos
de la mujer

Población Servida:
Mujeres jóvenes
de color
Juventud

CITIZEN ACTION OF NEW YORK-- LEAD POISONING OUTREACH PROGRAM

271 West 125th Street, Ste. 211
New York, NY 10027

Teléfono: 212-961-1135
Fax: 212-961-1015
Contacto: Zenaida Mendez,
Directora
Horario: 9am-5pm
Area Geográfica: Toda la ciudad

Foco de la Organización:
Promover el desarrollo de
movimientos de acción civica

Descripción General:
Somos una coalición de organizaciones dedicada a crear una voz bien
informada de acción civica para el
desarrollo y la aplicación de
programas y políticas efectivas sobre
el medio ambiente, el trabajo, los
ancianos, las mujeres, las gentes de
color, las comunidades y los
inquilinos.

Recursos: Boletín informativo,
folletos, videos, conferenciantes,
facilitadores de talleres y un local
para reuniones.
Reuniones: Sí.

Temas:
Justicia social
Medio ambiente

Población Servida:
Multiétnica

COALICION PARA GENTE SIN VIVIENDA

89 Chambers Street, 3rd Fl.
New York, NY 10007

Teléfono: 212-964-5900
Fax: 212-964-1303
Contacto: Mary Brosnahan,
               Directora Ejecutiva
Horario: 9am-6pm
Personal: Asalariado
Area Geográfica: Toda la ciudad

Foco de la Organización:
CFH es la organización de servicio
directo más antigua del país que lucha
para acabar con la falta masiva de
vivienda.

Descripción General:
Además de nuestra lucha pionera y
de nuestro activismo de base, CFH
lleva una docena de programas que
incluyen una cantina itinerante, un
campamento para niños sin vivienda,
alojamiento permanente para familias
e individuos sin vivienda y personas
con SIDA, entrenamiento laboral e
intervenciones de emergencia.

Recursos: Boletín informativo,
folletos, informes y espacio para
reuniones.
Reuniones: Sí. Reuniones mensuales
del Grupo de Consejo al Cliente
Organización de miembros: No

Temas: Población Servida:
Vivienda   Multiracial
Antiviolencia
VIH/SIDA
Salud
Justicia social

COMITE DE NUEVA YORK EN SOLIDARIDAD CON EL PUEBLO DE EL SALVADOR

19 West 21 Street, #502
New York, NY 10010

Teléfono: 212-645-5230
Fax: 212-645-7280
Contacto: Greg Wilpert,
               Coordinador
Personal: Asalariado
Area Geográfica: Toda la ciudad

Foco de la Organización: Solidaridad
con El Salvador

Descripción General:
Trabajar contra los esfuerzos de
Estados Unidos por dominar América
Latina y ayudar en la construcción de
una alternativa mediante la
democracia participatoria, derechos
humanos y justicia. CISPES se
esfuerza po desafiar el racismo,
sexismo, homofobia y otras formas
de opresión.

Recursos: Boletín informativo
Reuniones: Sí
Organización de miembros: No

Temas:
Justicia social
Solidaridad internacional
Antiracismo
Derechos de los trabajadores
Derechos de las mujeres

COMMISSION ON THE PUBLIC'S HEALTH SYSTEM

c/o Patient's Rights Hotline
215 West 125th Street, Rm. 400
New York, NY 10027-4426

Teléfono: 212-316-9393
Contacto: Nilka Alvarez,
                 Coordinadora
Horario: Lunes-Viernes, 9-5
Personal: Asalariado
Area Geográfica: Toda la ciudad.

Foco de la Organización:
Suministramos apoyo al sector público en materia de servicios y cuidado médicos para lograr una igualdad en el acceso y la calidad de servicios para todos los neoyorquinos.

Descripción General:
Somos una coalición de defensores de la salud pública, grupos de la comuni-dad, trabajores en el campo de la salud y pacientes que apoya las alternativas a la privatización de los servicios públicos y que esta comprometida a obtener servicios médicos para todos que sean accesibles, responsables y de calidad.

Recursos: Materiales informativos, referencias de oradores, talleres de entrenamiento sobre la salud.
Reuniones: Sí
Requisitos: Comprometerse a nuestras metas y aceptar nuestros principios.

Temas: Población Servida:
Salud   Multiétnica
                    Pobres

CONGRESO NORTEAMERICANO SOBRE AMERICA LATINA (NACLA)

475 Riverside Drive, Suite 454
New York, NY 100115

Teléfono: 212-870-3146
Fax: 212-870-3305
Contacto: Pierre M. LaRamée,
                 Director Ejecutivo
Horario: 9:30am- 5:30pm
Personal: Asalariado
Area Geográfica: América Latina

Descripción General:
El Congreso Norteamericano sobre América Latina, fundado en 1966, es un instituto editorial y de investigación que provee análisis detallados sobre la política exterior estadounidense en Latinoamérica y sobre las condiciones políticas, sociales y económicas en el interior de la región.

Multilingüe: inglés y francés

Recursos: Una publicación bimensual: "NACLA Report on the Americas"; una pequeña biblioteca centro de lectura y de investigación sobre las Américas; oradores, entrevistas, conferencias, etc.
Requisitos: Suscripción a la revista

Temas: Población Servida:
Solidaridad   Multiétnica
internacional   Activistas
Desarrollo   Políticos
económico   Periodistas
Antiracismo   Académicos
Medios de comunicación
Justicia social

COOPER SQUARE COMMITTEE

61 East 4th Street
New York, NY 10003

Teléfono: 212-228-8210
Fax: 212-477-5328
Contacto: Valerio Orselli,
               Director
Horario: Lunes-Viernes 9am-5pm
Personal: Asalariado
Area Geográfica: El bajo este de
Manhattan

Foco de la Organización:
Planificar y organizar para el
desarrollo y la preservación de
viviendas módicas

Descripción General:
Somos la organización más antigua en
los Estados Unido que combate
contra el desahucio.

Multilingüe: inglés, italiano y ukraino

Recursos: Boletín informativo,
folletos, videos, información sobre
los derechos de los inquilinos y
servicios sociales.
Reuniones: Al menos 3 veces al año
Organización de miembros: Sí
Requisitos: Todas las personas que
vivan en el area de renovación urbana
de Cooper Square.

Temas:	Población Servida:
Vivienda	Multiétnica
Desamparo	Clase trabajadora
Desarrollo	con bajos ingresos
económico	

COORDINADORA DE LA CULTURA POPULAR

63 South Portland Avenue
Brooklyn, NY 11217

Teléfono: No
Contacto: Soraya Marcano,
               Directora
Oficina: No
Personal: No

Foco de la Organización:
Artistas latinos.

Descripción General:
Organizamos a los artistas latinos
buscando la manera de presentar sus
obras a más gente. Esperamos
incrementar la solidaridad y el
intercambio entre los artistas y sus
comunidades.

Reuniones: No
Organización de miembros: No

Temas:	Población Servida:
Arte/Cultura	Latinos/Hispanos

COORDINADORES PARA LA CONSERVACION DE LA VIVIENDA (HCC)

777 10th Avenue
New York, NY 10019

Teléfono: 212-5415996
Fax: 212-541-5966
Contacto: Kyle E. Stewart
Horario: 9am-5pm
Personal: Asalariado
Area Geográfica: Clinton, Manhattan

Foco de la Organización: Prevención de la falta de vivienda y estabilización de barriadas mediante la defensa de los derechos de los inquilinos y asistencia técnica.

Descripción General:
HCC tiene 22 años de existencia. Posee 6 programas para conservar la composición de la población de Clinton (Hell's Kitchen), en su mayoría clase trabajadora, como acondicionamiento de edificios, préstamos para mejora de vivienda, instruccción técnica sobre reparaciones domésticas, administra-ción 7a, programa para la alimentación de ciudadanos de la tercera edad, asociación legal de vecinos.

Multilingüe: Español, francés

Recursos: Local de reuniones, facilitadores de talleres sobre vivienda y obtención de fondos.
Organización de miembros: No

Temas: Población Servida:
Vivienda   Multiracial
Legal
Justicia social

DEEP DISH TELEVISION NETWORK

339 Lafayette Street, 3rd Floor
New York, NY 10012

Teléfono: 212-473-8933
Fax: 212-420-8223
Contacto: Cynthia López
Horario: Martes, miércoles y
               viernes, 10am-6pm
Personal: Asalariado

Foco de la Organización:
Una red nacional via satélite de productores, defensores de los medios de comunicación, activistas y de organizaciones de acción cívica. Distribuimos programas via satélite a canales municipales, educacionales y de acceso público.

Descripción General:
Coproducimos y distribuimos programas que presentan a activistas confrontando temas como el medio ambiente, la vivienda y el desamparo, la justicia social y criminal, el racismo, los derechos civiles y el SIDA. Estos programas son producidos por jóvenes, mujeres, gays y lesbianas, trabajadores y ancianos.

Recursos: Videos.
Reuniones: No
Organización de miembros: No

Temas: Población Servida:
Medios   Multiétnica
de comunicación
Justicia social
Arte/Cultura

THE DOOR - A CENTER OF ALTERNATIVES

121 Avenue of the Americas
New York, NY 10013

Teléfono: 212-941-9090
Fax: 212-941-0714
Contacto: Kathleen Connolly, Directora del desarrollo
Horario: Lunes-Viernes 8am-6pm
Personal: Asalariado y voluntario
Area Geográfica: Toda la ciudad

Foco de la Organización:
Ofrecer servicios comprensivos e integrados a jóvenes entre los 12 y 21 años que se encuentran en situaciones desventajosas para que crezcan y maduren sanamente.

Descripción General:
Fundada en 1972 para asistir a jóvenes a que evitaran la burocracia del sistema de servicios sociales. Sus fundadores combinaron la experiencia de profesionales en diversas disciplinas para crear un instituto que actualmente brinda más de 20 programas y servicios para que satisfagan las necesidades de crecimiento de los adolescentes.

Multilingüe: chino, polaco y ruso

Recursos: Boletín informativo, folletos, programas educativos, asistencia técnica y excursiones.
Reuniones: No
Organización de miembros: No

Temas:	Población Servida:
Juventud	Jóvenes
Arte/Cultura	

EDUCADORES POR LA JUSTICIA SOCIAL

475 Riversida Drive, Room 450
New York, NY 10115

Teléfono: 212-8703318
Fax: 212-870-2264
Contacto: Michael Hirschhorn
Horario: 9am-5pm
Personal: Asalariado
Area Geográfica: Toda la ciudad

Foco de la Organización:
Hacer de la responsabilidad social una parte integral de la educación, divulgando nuevos métodos de enseñanza y aprendizaje.

Descripción General:
E.S.R. coordina programas a favor de la resolución de conflictos, la diversidad y la prevención de la violencia en 150 escuelas y organizaciones comunitarias. Entre sus proyectos se incluyen uno para la educación multicultural, escuelas educando sobre opciones para la paz, y el proyecto de entrenamiento organizativo con base en la comunidad.

Multilingüe: Chino, Criollo, Haitiano

Recursos: Boletines, facilitadores de talleres, folletos, vídeos, manuales creativos de enseñanza suplementaria.
Reuniones: Foros mensuales del Proyecto de Educación Multicultural
Organización de miembros: Sí
Cuota: $35

Temas:	Población Servida:
Educación	Multiracial
Antiracismo	Profesores
Antiviolencia	Administradores
Paz	Jóvenes

ELDERS SHARE THE ARTS

57 Willoughby Street
Brooklyn, NY 11201

Teléfono: 718-488-8565
Fax: 718-488-8296
Contacto: Susan Perlstein,
Directora
Horario: Lunes-Viernes 9-5
Personal: Asalariado y voluntario
Area Geográfica: Toda la ciudad

Foco de la Organización:
Entrelazar culturas y generaciones a través de "Artes de la Historia viviente"

Descripción General:
Nuestro equipo de artistas profesionales trabaja con personas de mayor edad y jóvenes para transformar las historias de sus vidas en presentaciones dramáticas, literarias y visuales que celebran la vida comunitaria. Compartimos las experiencias de vida de los artistas de mayor edad con las comunidades que tienen poco acceso al arte.

Multilingüe: inglés, chino

Recursos: Nuestro boletín "Cultural Connections" y manuales de entrenamiento, videos y cintas con ancianos que narran cuentos, local de reuniones, conferenciantes y talleres.
Organización de Miembros: Sí
Requisitos para ser miembro: $25

Temas: Población Servida:
Arte/Cultura   Personas mayores
Antiracismo   de edad
                       Jóvenes

ENVIRONMENTAL ACTION COALITION

625 Broadway, 2nd Floor
New York, NY 10012

Teléfono: 212-677-1601
Fax: 212-505-8613
Contacto: Steve Richardson,
Director Ejecutivo
Horario: Lunes-Viernes 9:30-6
Personal: Asalariado

Area Geográfica: Toda la ciudad

Foco de la organización:
Buscar soluciones prácticas y de posible aplicación para resolver problemas ambientales urbanos y trabajar para que estas soluciones sean adoptadas.

Descripción General:
EAC trabaja con organizaciones comunitarias y escuelas en los cinco condados de la ciudad de Nueva York para que los recursos e información sobre el medio ambiente estén al alcance de todos.

Recursos: Boletín, videos, folletos, hojas informativas sobre temas del medio ambiente.
Organización de miembros: Sí
Requisitos: Cuota anual de $20.

Temas: Población Servida:
Medio ambiente   Multiétnica
Educación   Jóvenes
Responsabilidad   Mujeres
del gobierno

ENVIRONMENTAL DEFENSE FUND

257 Park Avenue South
New York, NY 10010

Teléfono: 212-505-2100
Fax: 212-505-2375
Contacto: Barbara Olshansky,
              Abogada
Horario: 9am-6pm
Personal: Asalariado y voluntario
Area Geográfica: Toda la ciudad

Foco de la Organización:
Asuntos ambientales: polución, salud
pública, reforma reglamentaria,
participación ciudadana, conservación
de recursos naturales

Descripción General: Environmental
Defense Fund es una organización
nacional, no lucrativa de investigación
ambiental, educación y defensa
compuesta de abogados, científicos y
economistas.

Recursos: Folletos, estudios, videos,
salón de reuniones, oradores,
profesores de seminarios, boletín de
ciencia técnica, expertos, línea
telefónica sobre envenenamiento con
plomo.
Organización de Miembros: Sí
Requisitos: Cuota anual de $15.

Temas:
Medio ambiente
Responsabilidad del gobierno
Derechos humanos

FIFTH AVENUE COMMITTEE

199 Fourteenth Street
Brooklyn, NY 11215

Teléfono: 718-965-2777
Fax: 718-832-6676
Contacto: Brad Lander, Director
              Ejecutivo
Horario: Lunes-Viernes 9am-5pm
Personal: Asalariado
Area Geográfica: South B'klyn

Foco de la Organización:
FAC trabaja sobre temas de la
vivienda, los derechos de inquilinos,
el bienestar público, el desarrollo
económico de la comunidad y la
organización de la comunidad sobre
temas de interés para la vecindad.

Descripción General:
FAC trabaja para preservar y
fortalecer la diversidad económica,
racial y étnica del sur de Park Slope y
Brooklyn sur y para asegurar que
todos los residentes se beneficien del
desarrollo del area.

Recursos: Boletín, talleres sobre
viviendas módicas, derechos de
inquilinos, asistencia pública, toma de
poder.
Reuniones públicas: Sí, anunciadas en
el boletín
Organización de miembros: No

Temas: Población Servida:
Desarrollo   Multiétnica
económico   Latina/Hispana
Vivienda   Afro-Americana
Abogacía sobre
asistencia pública
Antiracismo

A GATHERING OF THE TRIBES

285 East 3rd Street
New York, NY 10009

Teléfono: 212-674-3778
Fax: 212-674-5576
Contacto: Steve Cannon,
Director
Horario: Informal
Personal: Voluntario
Area Geográfica: Toda la ciudad

Foco de la Organización:
Un grupo diverso de artistas de todas las generaciones que trabajan juntos para crear un futuro mejor.

Descripción General:
Nuestra organización participa con la comunidad exhibiendo obras de arte visual, auspiciando certámenes de poesía y talleres y produciendo obras de teatro. Nuestros objetivos son ganar una audiencia más amplia para nuestros artistas, atraer un nuevo público dentro de nuestras comunidades que jamás ha asistido a eventos artísticos y animar a nuevos artistas a que participen en nuestros proyectos.

Multilingüe: inglés, alemán, coreano, francés, indú, e italiano

Recursos: Computadoras, salón para ensayos, galeria y taller
Reuniones: El primer sábado del mes
Organización de miembros: No

Temas: Población Servida:
Arte/Cultura   Multiétnica

GLOBAL KIDS, INC.

561 Broadway, 6th floor
New York, NY 10012

Teléfono: 212-226-0130
Fax: 212-226-0137
Contacto: Carole Nichols,
Directora
Horario: 9am-5pm
Personal: Asalariado
Area Geográfica: Toda la cuidad

Foco de la Organización:
El desarrollo de la juventud

Descripción General:
Global Kids es una organización independiente, no lucrativa, dedicada al cultivo del conocimiento, los valores y el liderazgo necesarios para que los jóvenes puedan discutir temas de importancia en su comunidad y formar el futuro dentro de un mundo diverso culturalmente.

Multilingüe: ingles y francés

Recursos: Talleres entre los jóvenes, ejercicios dirigidos por, un congreso anual y videos internacionales producidos por los jóvenes, el desarrollo profesional para profesores y estudiantes.

Temas: Población Servida:
Juventud   Jóvenes
Antiracismo   Estudiantes
Antiviolencia   Multiétnica
Derechos   Educadores
humanos
Educación

H.E.L.P. BRONX, INC.

285 East 171 Street
Bronx, NY 10457

Teléfono: 718-583-0174
Fax: 718-583-9085
Contacto: Henry Beattie,
               Director de Servicios
               de Programación
Horario: 24 horas al día
Personal: Asalariado
Area Geográfica: Bronx, Brooklyn,
Manhattan

Foco de la Organización: Vivienda

Descripción General:
Somos la mayor organización
nacional que lleva refugios de Nivel II
para gente sin techo. Nos
mobilizamos también en contra de
cortes de presupuesto y abogamos a
favor de vivienda para los sin techo.

Recursos: Boletín informativo
Organización de miembros: No

Temas:..	Población Servida:
Vivienda	Multiracial

HOMBRES GAY/LATINOS DE NEW YORK

P.O. Box 1103
New York, NY 10025-1103

Teléfono: 212-663-9148
Contacto: J. Ramón Olmo, Junta
               Directiva
Personal: Voluntario
Area Geográfica: Toda la ciudad

Foco de la Organización:
Proveer un local seguro para
reuniones

Descripción General:
Proveer diversas actividades en un
local seguro para los 400 y más
hombres que reciben el boletín
informativo, que lista actividades
culturales, sociales, de salud,
derechos humanos/civiles y otras
actividades de interés e importancia
para cualquier miembro.

Multilingüe: inglés y portugués

Recursos: Conferenciantes, boletín,
agencias públicas de la ciudad y el
estado.
Organización de Miembros: Sí
Reuniones: Todos los primeros
viernes de cada mes. 8-10 p.m. en el
G&L Community Center 208 West
13th Street.

Temas:	Población Servida:
Educación	Hombres
Antiviolencia	Latino/Hispanos
Antiracismo	Multiétnica
Gay	Gay
VIH/SIDA	

HUDSON GUILD

441 West 26th Street
New York, NY 10001

Teléfono: 212-760-9804
Fax: 212-268-9983
Contacto: Janice McGuire,
             Directora Executiva
Horario: Lunes-Viernes 8am-6pm
Personal: Voluntario y asalariado
Area Geográfica: Chelsea, Manhattan

Foco de la Organización:
Hudson Guild es una agencia de
servicio multiple que trabaja para
proveer servicios y mejorar la
Comunidad de Chelsea.

Descripción General:
Además de tener una gran variedad
de servicios directos, la agencia
trabaja para facilitar y mantener los
esfuerzos de la comunidad.

Recursos: Local de reuniones con
prioridad para grupos locales.
Organización de miembros: Sí
Requisitos: Cuota anual de $5- $24

INSTITUTE FOR PUERTO RICAN POLICY (IPR)

236 Fifth Avenue, 3rd Floor
New York, NY 10001-4512

Teléfono: 212-564-1075
Fax: 212-564-1014
Contacto: Angelo Falcón,
             Presidente
Horario: 9:00am-5:00pm
Personal: Asalariado y voluntario
Area Geográfica: Toda la ciudad

Foco de la Organización:
Un instituto, sin motivo de lucro y
sin ninguna afiliación política, que fue
establecido en 1982 con el objetivo
de estudiar los problemas e intereses
de los portorriqueños y latinos.

Descripción General:
El instituto se especializa en investiga-
ciones sobre la guerrilla y se concentra
en tres areas: análisis político, participación cívica y la juxtaposición de
políticas. Nuestro método combina el
análisis técnico con los aspectos políticos en la formación de la política pública.

Recursos: Publicaciones sobre temas
portorriqueños como la revista
Crítica, el boletín informativo
Diálogo, reportajes especiales y la
publicación anual ¡Soy Boricua!
Reuniones: Sí
Organización de miembros: Sí

Temas:	Población Servida:
Responsabilidad	Multiétnica
gubernamental	Hispanos/Latinos
Justicia social	Portorriqueños
Derecho a votar	
Antiracismo	

JUVENTUD CONTRA EL RACISMO Y LA POBREZA

144 N. 9th Street, #31
Brooklyn, NY 11211

Teléfono: 718-963-2518
Fax: 718-956-7748
Personal: Voluntario
Area Geográfica: Toda la ciudad

Foco de la Organización:
Estudiantes de escuela secundaria,
universidad y la juventud trabajadora

Descripción General:
Luchamos por los derechos de la
juventud, con un programa que
incluye la reivindicación de un
empleo garantizado, educación
gratuita en todos los niveles y para
que se duplique el salario mínimo.
Organizamos en las escuelas, sitios de
trabajo y comunidades. Convocamos
manifestaciones y protestas como
método de lucha para mejorar
nuestras vidas y para desafiar al
poder establecido que considera a la
juventud como una molestia.

Recursos: Oradores, hojas volantes y
organizadores de diferentes eventos.
Miembros: Sí

Temas: Población Servida:
Juventud   Jóvenes
Racismo
Justicia social
Solidaridad internacional

KENSINGTON ACTION FORCE

4520 18th Avenue
Brooklyn, NY 11204

Teléfono: 718-435-1300
Fax: 718-282-8913
Contacto: Sidney Zelman,
              Coordinador/Director
Personal: Asalariado
Area Geográfica: Kensington,
Brooklyn

Foco de la Organización:
Elevar la calidad de vida en
Kensington mediante la educación de
la comunidad.

Descripción General:
Entre 16,000 y 64,000 residentes se
benefician de una variedad de
programas como patrullas voluntarias
del barrio, reuniones con la policía,
políticos y junta de comunidad para
exigir la atención de esos sectores a
la comunidad.

Multilingüe: Ruso, yiddish, español

Recursos: Boletín; exposición sobre
seguridad comunitaria (en
preparación)
Reuniones: 4 veces al año, en marzo,
mayo, septiembre y noviembre
Organización de miembros: Sí
Requisitos: Vivir en Kensington,
cuota de $25

Temas: Población Servida:
Crimen y justicia Todos los
Educación   residentes de
Antiviolencia   Kensington

LA ASOCIACION BENEFICA CULTURAL FATHER BILLINI

104-11 37th Avenue
Corona, NY 11368

Contacto: Ana López, Directora Executiva
Horario: 9-6pm
Personal: No
Area Geográfica: Toda la ciudad

Foco de la Organización:
Prestar servicios a residentes de la ciudad de Nueva York, en particular a jóvenes desventajados economicamente y a personas deficientes en inglés.

Descripción General:
Una organización sin fines de lucro, con servicios múltiples en los cinco condados y la agencia principal del centro comunitario Claridad Beacon que ofrece a toda la comunidad un amplio programa de actividades educativas, recreativas y vocacionales, consejería y referencias a otras agencias de servicio

Recursos: Lugar para reuniones, clases de inglés, educación para adultos y computadoras.

Reuniones: Sí, cada tres meses

Temas:	Población Servida:
Servicios juveniles	Jóvenes
	Latina/Hispana
Servicios para niños y familia	Multiétnica
Servicios de empleos e información	

LATINA ROUNDTABLE ON HEALTH AND REPRODUCTIVE RIGHTS

34 East 70th Street
New York, NY 10021

Teléfono: 212-628-6702
Fax: 212-861-1220
Contacto: Wilma Montañez, Directora
Oficina: Sí
Horario: 9:00am-5:00pm
Personal: Asalariado y voluntario
Area Geográfica: Toda la ciudad

Foco de la Organización:
Abogacía y difusión pública de los derechos de salud y reproducción de la mujer.

Descripción General:
Aumentar la difusión pública de los problemas de salud y los derechos reproductivos entre las latinas y apoyar las reformas necesarias en los ámbitos legislativo, judicial y administrativo que esten designadas a mejorar los servicios médicos y las opciones de reproducción.

Reuniones: No
Organización de miembros: No

Temas:	Población Servida:
Salud	Latinas
VIH/SIDA	
Derechos de la mujer	
Ejercicio del derecho de reproducción	

LATINO COMMISSION ON AIDS

80 Fifth Avenue
New York, New York 10011

Teléfono: 212-675-3288
Fax: 212-675-3466
Contacto: Juan Méndez, Director
Horario: 9:30am-5:30pm
Personal: Asalariado
Area Geográfica: Toda la ciudad

Foco de la Organización:
Fomentar la unión de la comunidad y desarrollar una política pública sobre la crisis del SIDA en la comunidad latina.

Descripción General:
Nuestros objetivos principales son la protección de las mujeres afectadas por el SIDA, el intercambio de jeringas para reducir el mal y la protección de prisioneros afectados por el SIDA.

Recursos: Salón de reuniones, boletín informativo y facilitadores de talleres.
Reuniones: Sí
Organización de miembros: Sí
Requisitos: Organizaciones latinas y latinos que trabajan contra el SIDA, latinos que tienen VIH o padecen del SIDA y los amigos de la comisión.

Temas: Población Servida:
VIH/SIDA   Caribeños
                  Latinos/Hispanos
                  Gay latinos y
                  lesbianas latinas

LATINO WORKERS CENTER

191 East 3rd Street
New York, NY

Teléfono: 212-973-3936
Fax: 212-473-6103
Contacto: Monica Santana
Horario: 10:00am-6:00pm
Personal: Asalariado
Area Geográfica: Toda la ciudad

Foco de la Organización:
Unir a los trabajadores latinos de todas las industrias para que juntos presten su apoyo a los esfuerzos de organizacion de cada uno de ellos.

Descripción General:
Una organización de miembros que esta dedicada a apoyar los esfuerzos de los trabajadores latinos a organizarse para obtener mejores condiciones de trabajo, lograr el respeto de sus derechos y darles la oportunidad de ser escuchados cuando se tomen decisiones que afecten sus vidas.

Recursos: Boletín informativo.
Reuniones: Sí, una cada mes.
Organización de miembros: Sí
Requisitos: Aceptar los principios declarados y pagar una cuota basada en una escala graduada

Temas: Población Servida:
Justicia social   Latinos/Hispanos
Derechos del Mujeres
trabajador/inmigrante
Derechos de la mujer

LATINOS Y LATINAS DE AMBIENTE/NY (LLANY)

c/o The L/G Community Center
208 West 13th Street
New York, New York 10011

Teléfono: 718-588-0201
Fax: 212-673-6128
Contacto: Frank J. Guzman
Personal: Voluntario
Area Geográfica: Toda la ciudad

Foco de la Organización:
Una organización socio-cultural para gay y lesbianas latinos que mejora nuestra visibilidad dentro de las comunidades gay y latina.

Descripción General:
Tenemos varios comités: el comité para el boletín informativo "Arco Iris Newsletter", el comité para recaudar fondos, el comité para el desarrollo de relaciones con los medios de información, el comité de cultura y educación y el comité Minealo/Dance.

Recursos: Boletín, video y oradores.
Reuniones: Sí, dos veces al mes.
Organización de miembros: Sí
Requisitos: Cuota anual de $25, asistencia regular y apoyo a la constitución y reglas de LLANY.

Temas:	Población Servida:
Homosexualismo	Gay latinos y
Justicia social	lesbianas latinas
Antiracismo	
Arte/Cultura	
VIH/SIDA	
Derechos humanos	

LAWYERS ALLIANCE FOR NEW YORK

99 Hudson Street, 14th Floor
New York, N Y 10013

Teléfono: 212-219-1800
Fax: 212-941-7458
Contacto: Janet R. Raiffa, Coordinadora del programa de reclutamiento pro bono
Personal: Asalariado
Area Geográfica: Toda la ciudad

Foco de la Organización:
Suministrar servicios legales gratuitos o a bajo costo -- en materia de bienes y raices, impuestos y sociedades anónimas -- a organizaciones que ofrecen sus servicios a comunidades con bajo rendimiento económico.

Descripción General:
A través de 3 programas ofrecemos nuestros servicios legales directamente y coordinamos las actividades de nuestros voluntarios que prestan asistencia legal gratuitamente.

Recursos: Boletín, servicio telefónico para responder a preguntas de tipo legal y talleres.
Reuniones: No
Organización de miembros: No

Temas:	Población Servida:
Desarrollo	Multiétnica
económico	
Vivienda	
Protección de	
menores	

LLAMADO INTERNA-CIONAL PAZ PARA CUBA

39 West 14th Street, #206
New York, NY 10011

Teléfono: 212-633-6646
Fax: 212-633-2889
Contacto: Teresa Gutierrez,
              Coordinadora
Personal: Voluntario
Area Geográfica: Toda la ciudad

Foco de la Organización:
Manifestar nuestra solidaridad con el pueblo cubano; luchar contra el bloqueo y las amenazas militares de los E.E.U.U.; recaudar ayuda material; y educar al pueblo norteamericano sobre Cuba.

Descripción General:
Organización activista que tiene reuniones, mítines, manifestaciones y más contra la agresión de los E.E.U.U. hacia Cuba y para manifestar nuestra solidaridad con el pueblo cubano.

Recursos: Periódicos, folletos, videos, conferenciantes, moderadores de talleres.

Temas: Población Servida:
Solidaridad   Multiétnica
internacional
Paz/Antimilitarismo
Antiracismo

MADRE

121 West 27th Street
New York, NY 10001

Teléfono: 212-627-0444
Fax: 212-675-0444
Contacto: Vivian Stromberg,
              Directora Ejecutiva
Horario: 9:30am-5:30pm
Personal: Asalariado
Area Geográfica: Toda la ciudad y el territorio nacional

Foco de la Organización:
Derechos humanos de la mujer

Descripción General:
Madre es una organización de mujeres que cuenta con 20,000 miembros de todas las razas y clases sociales. Nuestra meta es incrementar las posibilidades de paz y justicia a nivel nacional e internacional mediante la difusión de los derechos humanos de la mujer.

Recursos: Boletín, folletos, videos, oradores y un centro de documentación para mujeres.
Reuniones: Sí
Organización de miembros: Sí
Requisitos: Cuota de $25.00

Temas: Población Servida:
Derechos de   Multiétnica
la mujer
Derechos humanos

MFY LEGAL SERVICES, INC.

223 Grand Street
New York, NY 10013

Teléfono: 212-966-7410
Fax: 212-226-8584
Contacto: Stephen Myers, Dir.
Horario: Lunes-Viernes 9:30-5:30
Personal: Asalariado
Area Geográfica: Manhattan, las
partes al sur de la calle Houston y al
este de la calle Brodaway

Foco de la Organización:
Ofrecer consejos legales y, donde sea
apropiado y posible, prestar
representación a individuos pobres
que viven en nuestro vecindario de
acción.

Descripción General:
La mayor parte de nuestros servicios
legales esta relacionada con
propietarios e inquilinos y con
beneficios gubernamentales.
También nos ocupamos de ciertos
casos de inmigración y derecho
familiar.

Multilingüe: cantonés, mandarino,
inglés y toisanés

Recursos: Prestación limitada de
oradores
Reuniones: No
Organización de miembros: No

Temas:
Vivienda
Protección del derecho a asistencia
pública

NATIONAL LABOR COMMITTEE IN SUPPORT OF WORKERS & HUMAN RIGHTS IN CENTRAL AMERICA

15 Union Square
New York, NY 10003

Teléfono: 212-242-0700
Fax: 212-255-7230
Contacto: Ralph Rivera, Director
Horario: Regular
Personal: Asalariado

Foco de la Organización:
Defender y promover los derechos
humanos del trabajador.

Descripción General:
Para realizar nuestros objetivos
conducimos pericias que entrelazan
los derechos del trabajador con
programas de asistencia extranjera;
auspiciamos campañas de educación
en los E.E.U.U. sobre los derechos
humanos del trabajador; y
organizamos redes de emergencia
que velen por violaciones y que
interpongan apelaciones en nombre
de trabajadores extranjeros cuyos
derechos o vidas estan en peligro.

Recursos: Reportajes especiales
Reuniones: No
Organización de miembros: No

Temas:
Derechos del trabajador
Derechos humanos
Solidaridad internacional

THE NEW YORK STREET THEATER CARAVAN

161-04 Jamaica Avenue
Jamaica, NY 11432

Teléfono: 718-657-8070
Horario: Jueves-Viernes 12-6pm
Contacto: Marcia Donalds,
             Asistente al Director
Personal: Asalariado y voluntario
Area Geográfica: Toda la ciudad

Foco de la Organización:
Crear un alto nivel de calidad en el
teatro y traer obras con un
significado relevante y social para un
público que carece de recursos
económicos para asistir a eventos
culturales comerciales.

Descripción General:
Uno de los más originales teatros
que ha nacido de la angustia y las
luchas de los años 70 contra la guerra
de Vietnam y por los derechos
civiles. Facilitamos el diálogo entre
los artistas y el público, enfrentamos
problemas y desarrollamos una visión
social.

Multilingüe: inglés, ruso y polaco

Recursos: Boletín, talleres y videos
Reuniones: No
Organización de miembros: Sí

Temas: Población Servida:
Arte/Cultura   Multiétnica
Justicia social   Indígenas
Medio ambiente   Incapacitados
Derechos   Mujeres
humanos

NICARAGUA SOLIDARITY NETWORK

338 Lafayette Street #8
New York, NY 10012

Teléfono: 212-674-9499
Fax: 212-674-9139
Contacto: David B. Wilson
Pesonal: Voluntario
Area Geográfica: Toda la ciudad

Foco de la Organización:
Proveer información sobre Nicaragua
y Latinoamérica desde una
perspectiva izquierdista y de
movimientos populares.

Descripción General:
Trabajamos en coalición con latinos y
grupos solidarios, publicamos el
*Weekly News Update on the
Americas*, un boletín semanal con
resumen de noticias que cubre los
eventos en Latinoamérica y el Caribe.
También producimos semanalmente
un mensaje por radio de 7 minutos.

Recursos: Boletín de noticias;
volantes informativos, calendario de
actividades, archivo de fuentes
informativas, archivos
computarizados de datos.

Temas:
Solidaridad internacional

PARTIDO INDEPENDENTISTA PUERTORRIQUEÑO

PO Box 1481 Gracie Station
New York, NY 10028

Teléfono: 212-860-7655
Contacto: Juan Rodríguez
Personal: Voluntario
Area Geográfica: Toda la ciudad

Foco de la Organización:
La independencia de Puerto Rico
mediante el proceso electoral y la
negociación con el Congreso de los
Estados Unidos.

Descripción General:
Nuestro partido nacional, fundado in
1946, tiene su sede principal en
Puerto Rico.Nos hemos establecido
aquí desde 1993 para organizar a los
miles de puertorriqueños que están a
favor de la independencia, y para fortalecer la solidaridad entre las organizaciones progresistas y de izquierda en
Nueva York y en los Estados Unidos.

Recursos: Periódico *El Antillano*;
conferenciantes y talleres infor-
mando sobre la historia, política,
cultura y luchas de los puertorriqueños.
Reuniones: Cada dos meses
Organización de miembros: Sí
Requisitos: Estar dedicado a la lucha
pacífica por la independencia de
Puerto Rico y a la ideología y
posiciones de nuestro partido.

Temas: Población Servida:
Justicia Social   Latina/Hispana
Antiracismo   Caribeña
Antiviolencia   Multiracial

PROGRAMA DE INTERVENCION CONTRA LA VIOLENCIA DOMESTICA

P.O. Box 136, Triborough Station
New York, NY 10035

Teléfono: 212-360-5090
Fax: 212-410-9117
Contacto: Grace Perez, Directora
             Ejecutiva
Horario: Lun-Vier, 9-5pm
Personal: Asalariado
Area Geográfica: East Harlem

Foco de la Organización:
Programa de violencia doméstica,
basado en la comunidad y dirigido
hacia la mujer latina maltratada.

Descripción General:
Provee intervención en momentos
de crisis, consejería a largo/corto
plazo, información y servicios de
abogacía

Recursos: Línea de teléfono
permanente
Organización de Miembros: No

Temas: Población Servida:
Antiviolencia   Mujeres latinas
Derechos de
la mujer

PROJECT REACH

1 Orchard Street, 2nd Floor
New York, NY 10002

Teléfono: 212-966-4227
              1-800-70-REACH
Fax: 212-966-4963
Contacto: Don Kao
Horario: Lun-Vier, 10-6pm
Personal: Asalariado
Area Geográfica: Toda la ciudad

Foco de la Organización:
Enseñar a los jóvenes a comprender
las instituciones que los obstaculizan
y fomentar las relaciones con otros
jóvenes para cambiar las condiciones
que los oprimen.

Descripción General:
Un centro dirigido por jóvenes y
adultos de todas las razas que entrena
a los jóvenes para conver-tirlos a su
vez en consejeros de otros jóvenes
para que luchen contra la
discriminación.

Multilingüe: inglés y chino

Recursos: Salón de reuniones,
oradores, facilitadores de talleres y
asistencia técnica.
Reuniones: No
Organización de miembros: No

Temas: Población Servida:
Antiracismo   Multiétnica
VIH/SIDA   Jóvenes
Justicia criminal   Gays y lesbianas
y familiar

PROYECTO DE PARTICIPACION DE VOTANTES EN EL BRONX

2432 Grand Concourse, Rm. 504
Bronx, NY 10458

Teléfono: 718-365-5071
Fax: 718-584-3258
Contacto: Nina Laboy, Directora
Horario: 9am-5pm
Personal: Asalariado
Area Geográfica: South Bronx

Foco de la Organización:
Registración no partidista de
votantes, educación, participación
electoral y toma de poder de la
comunidad.

Descripción General:
Somos un proyecto de la Sociedad
para el Servicio Comunitario de
Nueva York. El proyecto cree que
los residentes de bajos ingresos
pueden luchar eficazmente por una
mejor representación en el gobierno
y por la mejora de los servicios
municipales, siempre que entiendan
cómo funciona el sistema político y
desarrollen sus facultades
organizativas.

Recursos:
Talleres y foros para la información
sobre derechos electorales, espacio
para reuniones, y asistencia técnica.
Organización de miembros: No

Temas: Población Servida:
Educación   Multiracial
Responsabilidad del Gobierno
Justicia social

PUEBLO EN MARCHA

401 East 145 Street
Bronx, NY 10454

Teléfono:	718-665-7375
Contacto:	Maximino Rivera, Director Ejecutivo
Horario:	9am-5pm
Personal:	Asalariado y voluntario

Area Geográfica: Zona del
Community Building #1 en el Bronx

Foco de la Organización:
Está dedicada a la mejora de la
comunidad en vivienda, juventud, y
servicios alimentarios de emergencia
para familias y la tercera edad.

Descripción General:
Entre los servicis ofrecidos se
incluyen: información,
recomendaciones y ayuda, vivienda y
servicio social, ayuda en situaciones
de emergencia en cuanto a comida
(despensa) y ropa. El Youth Advisory
Council lleva en el barrio el Youth
Alliance Program.

Recursos: Talleres sobre vivienda,
local de reuniones, folletos.
Reuniones públicas regulares: Llame
para preguntar por horario.
Organización de miembros: No

Temas:	Población Servida:
Vivienda	Afro-Americana
Juventud	Latina/Hispana

PUERTO RICAN LEGAL DEFENSE AND EDUCATION FUND

99 Hudson Street, Suite 1401
New York, NY 10013

Teléfono:	212-219-3360
	800-328-2322
Fax:	212-431-4276
Contacto:	Juan A. Figueroa, Presidente
Horario:	9:00am-5:00pm
Personal:	Asalariado

Area Geográfica: Toda la ciudad

Foco de la Organización:
Garantizar que cada puertorriqueño
y latino tenga la oportunidad de
superarse. Mediante la abogacía, la
educación y el proceso de causas,
PRLDEF protege los derechos
económicos, políticos, sociales y
legales de nuestra comunidad.

Descripción General:
Proteger los derechos civiles de los
latinos; luchar contra la pobreza y la
discriminación; mejorar la educación,
el empleo público, la vivienda y el
cuidado médico; aumentar el acceso
de minorías a las facultades de
derecho; y entrenar abogados.

Recursos: Boletín, folletos, salón de
reuniones, oradores y referencias de
abogados
Reuniones: No
Organización de miembros: No

Temas:	Población Servida:
Derechos humanos	Latinos/Hispanos

RIPTIDE COMMUNICATIONS, INC.
666 Broadway, Suite 444
New York, NY 10012

Teléfono: 212-260-5000
Contacto: David Lerner,
               Vicepresidente
Horario: 10:00am-6:00pm
Personal: Asalariado
Area Geográfica: Toda la ciudad

Foco de la Organización:
Proveer relaciones públicas a
individuos y grupos progresistas.

Descripción General:
La representación de clientes ante la
prensa, la presentación de
información y el adiestramiento en
relaciones públicas.

Reuniones: No
Organización de miembros: No

Temas:
Medios de comunicación
Métodos de organización

SERVICIOS LEGALES MFY, INC.
41 Avenue A
New York, NY 10009

Teléfono: 212-475-8000
Fax: 212-475-1043
Contacto: Wayne G. Hawley,
               Director Ejecutivo
Horario: 9:30am-5:30pm
Personal: Asalariado
Area Geográfica: East Side en
Manhattan, y el Westside desde
West 34th a 110th

Foco de la Organización:
Asegurar el acceso a la justicia de los
neoyorquinos pobres, aunque no
puedan pagarse un abogado

Descripción General:
MFY proporciona servicios legales de
alta calidad y servicio social en
asuntos civiles a individuos con
ingresos bajos, a familias y a grupos
en las comunidades de la ciudad de
las que se ocupa. MFY protege a sus
clientes reforzando las leyes
existentes, abogando por cambios en
las leyes, y educando a la comunidad.

Recursos: Folletos
Organización de miembros: No

Temas:	Población Servida:
Legales	Personas de bajos
Vivienda	ingresos
Defensa	Residentes en
del welfare	Manhattan

SERVICIOS PARA LA VIDA FAMILIAR ALONZO DAUGHTRY

415 Atlantic Avenue
Brooklyn, NY 11217

Teléfono: 718-596-3454
Fax: 718-625-3410
Contacto: Leah Daughtry,
              Directora Ejecutiva
Horario: 9:30am-5:30pm
Personal: Asalariado y vountario

Foco de la Organización:
Prestar servicios sociales y ayudar a los indigentes en comunidades de color.

Descripción General:
ADFLS enfoca sus servicios en forma global, identificando las necesidades de la gente en las comunidades de las que se ocupa, desarrollando y empleando métodos ya sean tradicionales o innovativos para satisfacer estas necesidades.

Recursos: Salón de reuniones y oradores

Reuniones: Martes por la tarde a las 7pm.
Organización de miembros: No

Temas:	Población Servida:
Servicio social	Afro-Americana
Toma de poder	Caribeña
	Mujeres
	Juventud

THORPE FAMILY RESIDENCE

2252 Crotona Avenue
Bronx, NY 10457

Teléfono: 718-933-7312
Fax: 718-933-7311
Contacto: Hermana B. Lenniger,
              Directora Ejecutiva
Personal: Asalariado y voluntario
Area Geográfica: Crotona, Bronx

Foco de la Organización: Alojamiento temporal para madres e hijos sin vivenda

Descripción General:
Permitir que las mujeres vivan independientemente en viviendas permanentes, concluyan sus estudios y mantengan trabajo. Impartimos educación y conocimientos sobre la política pública.

Mutlilingüe: inglés, francés y creol

Recursos: Boletín, hojas volantes, facilitadores

Temas:	Población Servida:
Vivienda	Las madres con hijos sin hogar

THE VALLEY INC.

1047 Amsterdam Avenue
New York, NY 10025

Teléfono: 212- 222-2110
Fax: 212- 222-4671
Contacto: James Murray,
               Director de Desarrollo
Horario: 8:00am-6:00pm
Personal: Asalariado
Area Geográfica: Toda la ciudad

Foco de la Organización:
Prestar servicios a jóvenes y sus
familias: servicios sociales y
programas recreacionales.

Descripción General:
Una agencia que presta servicios
múltiples a jóvenes (de 14 a 24 años)
con el objetivo de ayudarles a
convertirse en hombres y mujeres
autosuficientes, independientes y
responsables. Ofrecemos programas
en educación, trabajo, artes creativas,
asesoramiento y desarrollo de
características de liderazgo.

Recursos: Hoja informativa, talleres,
folletos, conferencias, referencias y
videos.
Reuniones: septiembre-junio, lunes-
jueves, 5-7pm
Organización de Miembros: No

Temas:	Población Servida:
Jóvenes	Jóvenes
Educación	Afroamericanos
Antiviolencia	Latinos/Hispanos
Antiracismo	Estudiantes
	Asiáticos/Islas del
	Pacífico

WOMEN FOR RACIAL & ECONOMIC EQUALITY

198 Broadway, #606
New York, NY 10038

Teléfono: 212-385-1103
Contacto: Ismay Harrigan,
               Directora en NY
Personal: Asalariado y voluntario
Area Geográfica: Toda la ciudad y el
territorio nacional

Foco de la Organización:
Una de las primeras organizaciones
progresistas de mujeres fundada en
los años 70 con el objetivo de
promover los intereses de la mujer
trabajadora de todas las razas. WREE
trata de reinstaurar estos intereses
dentro de los objetivos del
movimiento tradicional de las
mujeres en los Estados Unidos.

Descripción General:
Una organización multiétnica que
concentra sus esfuerzos en
problemas étnicos y de clases
sociales.

Recursos: Boletín, oradores,
facilitadores de talleres y
conferencias
Reuniones: De septiembre a mayo
Requisitos: Cuota anual basada en
ingreso percibido.

Temas:	Población Servida:
Salud	Mujeres
Antiracismo	Multiétnica
Derechos de la mujer	
Desarrollo económico	
Derechos del trabajador	

WOMENCARE, INC.

322 Eighth Avenue, suite 1700
New York, NY 10001

Teléfono: 212-463-9500
Fax: 212-463-0477
Contacto: Eileen Hogan,
                Directora Ejecutiva
Horario: 9:00am-5:00pm
Personal: Asalariado y voluntario
Area Geográfica: Toda la ciudad

Foco de la Organización:
WomenCare es un programa de
abogacía y asesoramiento para
madres que salen de la cárcel.

Descripción General:
WomenCare ofrece a madres la
oportunidad de desarrollar una
relación con un asesor voluntario
cuya base es la confianza mútua para
efectuar una transición exitosa
dentro de la comunidad.

Recursos: Folletos, oradores y
adiestramientos
Reuniones: Sí, usualmente el
primer martes de cada mes
Organización de miembros: No

Temas:	Población Servida:
Justicia social	Mujeres
y criminal	Jóvenes
VIH/SIDA	Multiétnica
Vivienda	
Protección del derecho	
a asistencia pública	
Derechos de la mujer	

YOUTH AGENDA

300 W. 43rd Street, 3rd Floor
New York, NY 10036

Teléfono: 212-977-5455
Contacto: Keith Hyman, Organ-
                izador de jóvenes
Horario: 10:00am-6:00pm
Personal: Voluntario
Area Geográfica: Toda la ciudad

Foco de la Organización:
Una coalición de jóvenes, maestros,
activistas de la comunidad y personas
que trabajan con la gente joven.

Descripción General:
Organizar varias manifestaciones,
conferencias de prensa, visitas
legislativas y velas para presionar a
nuestros representantes políticos a
que desarrollen programas que velen
por los intereses de la gente joven y
sus familias.

Multilingüe: chino (varios dialectos),
coreano, creol, inglés y patois

Recursos: Boletín, salón de reuniones
y adiestramientos.
Reuniones: Sí
Organización de miembros: Sí
Requisitos: Jóvenes, agencias, com-
pañias e individuos que consideran el
bienestar de la juventud como una de
sus responsabilidades.

Temas:	Población Servida:
Educación	Multiétnica
Salud	Jóvenes
HIV/SIDA	
Vivienda	
Derecho a asistencia pública	

YOUTH COMMUNICATION

144 West 27th Street, 8R
New York, NY 10001

Teléfono: 212-242-3270
Fax: 212-242-7057
Contacto: Keith Hefner, Director
Horario: Lunes-Viernes 8:30-6pm
Personal: Asalariado
Area Geográfica: Toda la ciudad

Foco de la Organización:
Ofrecer una voz a los adolescentes a través de la publicación de una revista escrita por ellos mismos.

Descripción General:
Youth Communication entrena a adolescentes en el arte del periodismo y publica dos revistas que circulan por toda la ciudad: New York Connections y Foster Care Youth United leídas por 200,000 adolescentes.

Multilingüe: chino, mandarino e inglés

Recursos: Boletín informativo
Reuniones: No
Organización de miembros: No

Temas: Población Servida:
Juventud   Juventud
Medios de comunicación
Estudiantes
Justicia social

YOUTH FORCE

300 West 43rd Street, 3rd Floor
New York, NY 10036

Teléfono: 212-977-5455
Contacto: Henry Diaz
Horario: 10am-9pm
Personal: Asalariado y voluntario
Area Geográfica: Toda la ciudad

Foco de la Organización:
Jóvenes que enseñan a otros jóvenes la fuerza, la capacidad y el derecho a ser escuchados y a fomentar el cambio.

Descripción General:
Organizar campañas para que jóvenes mejoren sus escuelas o vecindarios; ayuden a otros jóvenes; y cambien toda política pública ajena a sus intereses.

Multilingüe: coreano e inglés

Recursos: Videos, materiales, adiestramientos, consejeros y programas para convencer a jóvenes a que abandonen el tráfico de drogas.
Reuniones: Sí
Organización de miembros: Sí
Requisitos: Cualquier joven que esté comprometido a crear una mejor ciudad para todos los neoyorquinos.

Temas: Población Servida:
Justicia social   Multiétnica
Educación   Jóvenes en cuidado
VIH/SIDA   ajeno o que
Antiracismo   tengan o hayan
Derechos   tenido problemas
humanos   con la justicia
Antiviolencia   Gays y lesbianas

YOUTH UPRISING

300 West 43rd Street, 3rd Floor
New York, NY 10036

Teléfono: 212-977-5455
Contacto: Song Park
Area Geográfica: Toda la ciudad

Foco de la Organización:
Dar una voz pública e independiente a la juventud.

Descripción General:
Auspiciar campañas para 1) reestructurar el departamento de policía de la ciudad de Nueva York 2) mejorar la representación e imagen juvenil con los medios de comunicación y 3) unir a los jóvenes a través de programas de intercambio juvenil para explorar temas como la xenofobia, el nacionalismo y la democracia.

Multilingüe: coreano e inglés

Recursos: Activistas y abogados de experiencia que prestan su apoyo y ofrecen consejos y adiestramientos que enseñan la desobediencia civil.
Reuniones: No
Organización de miembros: Sí
Requisitos: Cualquier joven radical e independiente que tenga el coraje de cambiar la sociedad y el corazón para asegurarse que el cambio sea lo mejor para esta.

Temas:	Población Servida:
Antiracismo	Multiétnica
Medios de	Jóvenes
comunicación	Estudiantes
Justicia social	
Derechos humanos	

AMANAKA'A AMAZON NETWORK

584 Broadway, Room 814
New York, NY 10012

Téléphone: 212-925-5299
Fax: 212-925-7743
Contact: Zezé Weiss, Président
Horaire: de 10 à 18 heures
Personnel: Salarié et volontaires

Portée Général:
Dediqué à l'éducation du publique américain sur la forêt Amazonique et ses peuples.

Lanques Parlées: portugais, espagnol et français

Ressources: revue, videos, facilitateurs de seminaires, éspace pour réunions.
Réunions: Semaine de l'Amazone chaque printemps
Organisation de membres: Oui
Requis: US $25 par année ou US $35 pour deux années

Issues qui constituent l'organisation: environnement, éducation, droits humains
Support a: Peuples de la forêt

COALITION NATIONALE POUR LES REFUGIES HAITIENS

275 Seventh Ave. 25th Floor
New York, NY 10001

Téléphone: 212-337-0005
Fax: 212-337-0028
Contact: Jocelyn McCalla,
              Directeur Exécutif
Horaire: 9:00 am à 5:00 pm
Personnel: Payè
Portée géographique: La Metropole de New York

Objectif:
Promotion des Droits Humains et de la Justice

Description Générale:
La Coalition Nationale pour les Réfugiés Haitiens (CNRH) rassemble en son sein quelques grandes organisations américaines qui s'occupent des droits civils, syndicaux, religieux et des droits des immigrants. La CNRH entend défendre le droit des postulants Haitiens à l'asile politique et mène campagne en faveur des droits humains en Haiti et en faveur des Haitiens aux Etats-Unis.

Langues Parlées: creole haitien, français, anglais.

Ressources: Bulletins d'informations, rapports, publications sèminaires et conferences
Organisation de membres: Oui
Secteurs d'activités: Droits humains, Droits des immigrants, Justice sociale, Developpement économique (Haiti)

FOUNDATION FOR AFRICAN AMERICAN WOMEN

55 W. 68th Street
New York, NY 10023

Téléphone : 212-799-0322
Contat: Antonia C. Martin
Horaire: 9:00 a.m. à 5:00 p.m.
Portée Géographique: Toute la ville

Concentration de l'Organisation: Les femmes, la philantrophie et la justice sociale.

Description Générale:
Une organisation sans profit fondée en 1990 qui s'occupe de l'histoire et du futur des femmes Afro-Americaines. La fondation supporte des projets et des initiatives de femmes et de jeunes filles noires. Nous sommes très actives pour la loutte vers l'égalité sexuelle et raciale.

Langues Parlées: Le français, l'espagnol, et l'anglais

Ressources: Brochure.
Organisation des membres? No
Issues qui constituent l'organisation: Les issues concernant toutes les femmes et les femmes noires; telles que les droits reproductifs et la justice sociale.

HAITI SOLIDARITY NETWORK

202 East 32nd Street
Brooklyn, NY 11226

Téléphone :   718-856-5277
Fax: 718-284-5320
Contat: M. Jean D. Vernt, II
                  Directeur
Bureau: Non
Personnel: Volontaire
Portée Géographique; La zone metropolitaine

Objectifs:
Fondée en 1991, HSN offre certains services de naturalisation; des séminaires sur des sujets d'importance à la communauté, par exemple: comment voter, l'histoire des noirs aux Étas-Unis, et, des ateliers de travail sur la gestion et le developpement des organisationes.

Langues Parlées: anglais et creole

Ressources: Conferenciers sur les questions Haitiennes; animateurs de séminaires et d'ateliers.
Membres: Oui
Critères: Supporter les objectifs de l'organisation
Sujets d'intérêt: Droits de l'homme; droits des immigrants; solidarité internationale; droits de vote et droits des travailleurs.
Populations Ciblés: Haitiens, antillais Africain-Américains

475 Riverside Dr., Suite 454
New York, NY 10115

Téléphone : 212-870-3146
Fax: 212-870-3305
Contact: Pierre M. LaRamée,
Directeur Executif
Horaire: 9:30am-5:30pm
Personnel: Payé

Portée Générale:
L'Amérique Latine, fondée en 1966,
c'est une institution de recherche et
investigation devoue á l'analyse en
profondeur à la fois de la politique
étrangere des États-Unis envers
L'Amérique Latine, et de la condition
sociale, politique et économique de la
région.

Langues Parlées: espagnol et français

Ressources: Publication bimensuelle,
petite biblioteque et salle de lecture
sur les Amériques; conferences,
orateurs, entrevues, etc. NACLA
offre les ressources essentielles pour
établir une conscience publique
critique de la politique et de la
pratique des États-Unis dans la
région.
Réunions: Oui
Organisation de Membres: Oui
Exigences d'adhesion: Souscription a
la publication
Sujets: Solidarité internationale,
Reseaux de communication,
Developpement économique, Justice
sociale, Anti-racisme
Constituants: Multiracial, Activistes,
Politiciens, Journalistes, Académiciens

KOALISYON NASYONAL POU REFIJYE AYISYEN

275 7th Ave., 25th Fl.
New York, NY 10001

Telefòn: 212 337-0005
Fax: 212-337-0028
Kontak: Jocelyn McCalla, Direktè
c Ekzekitif
Biwo: Wi
Lètavay: 9e nan mate pou 5 nan aprèmidi
Anpwaye: Peye
Zòn Entevansyon: Nouyok
Bi òganizasyon-an: Pwomosyon Dwa Moun ak Jistis

Ki sa Oganizasyon-an ye? Koalisyon Nasyonal pou Refijye Ayisyen se youn alians kèK nan pi gwo oganizasyon ameriken ki ap travay nan domèn dwa sivil, sendika, legliz, ak dwa imigran. Oganizasyon an travay pou garanti jistis pou tout Ayisyen ki ap chache azil, pou fè respekte dwa moun an Ayiti, epou pwogre Ayisyen k ap viv Ozetazini.

Lang yo pale: Kreyol Ayisyen, Franse, Angle

Resous Oganizasyon-an: Bilten enformasyon, rapo, pibikasyon, semine ak konferans
Sou ki sa Oganizasyon an travay: Dwa moun, Dwa imigran, Jistis sosyal, Devlopman ekonomik (Haiti)

SANT AYISYEN POU ENFÒMASYON AK DOKIMANTASYON

1218 Flatbush Avenue
Brooklyn, NY 1126

Telefòn: 718-284-0889
Fax: 718-284-2545
Moun pou Kontaket: Daniel Huttinot, prezidan
Ernst Banatte, trezorye
Lè Blow: 12-9:30 pm
Staff: Volontè
Zòn jewografik: East Flatbush
Konsantrasyon Oganizasyonèl: Sant kominotè Ayisyen

Deskripsyon Jeneral: Sant Ayisyen Emfòmasyon ak Dokinamtasyon ofri sèvis varye tankou kou Anglè, konpitè ak kreyòl, leson patikilyè, tradiksyon dokiman, referans sou diferan kesyon tankou dwa imigrasyon; konferans sou sijè sa yo-- Ayiti, koze fanm, travayè ak dwa moun. Sant lan gen yon biblyotèk ki genyen dokiman sou Ayiti, keksyon fanm, travay'è ad moun.

Miltilang: Franse, Angle

Miting Piblik Regilye: Wi
Oganizasyon ak Manb: non
Sijè: Edikasyon Dwa monun Dwa imigran Pwoblè legal Medya-- pwogram radyo
Kliyantè: Karibeyen Milti-rasyal

紐約市亞美聯合會

紐約市 麥迪遜大道95號 1309室
95 Madison Avenue, #1309
New York, NY 10016

電話號碼： 212-725-3840
電傳真： 212-725-6629
聯系人： Cao O, 執行主任

辦公時間： 周一至周五 上午9點至下午5點
工作人員： 領取薪金
服務地區： 紐約市全市

服務宗旨： 利用各種社區設施和資源，激發社區
領袖的關注以協助提高亞裔美國人的生活
品質

組織概述： 紐約市亞美聯合會為一非贏利會員性
組織，她由各種健康與民眾服務機構聯合
組成，以滿足紐約市亞美民眾的需要。

服務資源： 聯合會新聞簡報，為會員組織提供開
會場地（非會員組織也可申請），各種亞
美裔資料和信息，工作間活動以及圖書館

該會為會員性組織
入會所需： 參照 501(C)(3)組織條例

關注之問題： 民眾和民權服務、選舉權、老年人服
務

服務對象： 亞洲及太平洋群島各族裔和老年人

亞美法律保護與教育基金會

紐約市 哈德遜大街 99號 12層
99 Hudson Street, 12Fl.
NewYork, NY, 10013

電話號碼：	212-966-5932
電傳真：	212-966-4303
聯系人：	Margaret Fung, 執行主任

辦公時間：	上午9：30至下午5：30
工作人員：	領取薪金
服務地區：	紐約市全市

服務宗旨：　法律事務與民權事務

組織概述：　亞美法律保護與教育基金會為亞裔社區參
與社會就民眾同時邁進勞工權利，美法律保護與教育對亞裔社區民眾提供法律教育。該會同時維護勞工權利，
提供訴訟事務反暴力行為，維護二戰期間日裔損失，
區民權益對選舉權利，賠償二戰期間日裔損失，
預維護以及維護就業與工作環境公平等活動。

雙語服務：　中文、韓文、日文

服務資源：　宣傳手冊、法律規範以及講演員

該會為會員性組織
入會所需：　參預支持該會活動

關注之問題：　法律、社會公正、選舉權、勞工權利
、移民權利

服務對象：　亞洲及太平洋群島各族裔

社會責任教育會

紐約市 河邊路475號 第450號房間
475 Riverside Drive, Room 450
New York, NY, 10115

電話號碼：	212-870-3318
電傳真：	212-870-2464
聯系人：	Michael Hirschhorn 副主任
辦公時間：	上午9：00至下午5：00
工作人員：	領取薪水
服務地區：	紐約市全市

服務宗旨： 倡導新的教育與學習方法，把培養社會責任感作為整個教育的一部分

組織概述： 該教育會在150所學校和社區組織設有化解糾紛和爭議，防止暴力的教育課程。具體內容包括多種文化傳統教育，如何以非暴力方式解決矛盾，以及為社區組織培訓人員。

雙語服務： 西班牙語、中文、海地法語

服務資源： 新聞簡報、輔導員培訓班、手冊、錄影帶以及各種教學設備

定期集會： 每月舉行一次公開的多種文化教育座談會

該會為會員性組織
入會所需： 35美元

關注之問題： 教育、反種族歧視、反暴力行為、青年問題、和平解決糾紛

亞美平等協會

紐約市 戴維森街 111號
111 Division Street
New York, NY, 10002

電 話 號 碼 :	212-964-2288
電 傳 真 :	212-964-6003
聯 系 人 :	Scott Ito.　　執行助理

辦 公 時 間 : 　上午9：00至下午5：00
工 作 人 員 : 　領取薪金
服 務 地 區 : 　中國城以及下東城地區

服 務 宗 旨 : 　　低收入住宅之開發和管理、經濟開發
、食品發放、入籍考試班、青少年領袖培
訓班以及其它為老年人和移民的服務

組 織 概 述 : 　　該協會旨在保護和倡導亞裔和其他有
色人種在以下方面的權利：民權、康價住
房、經濟發展和其它社會服務

雙 語 服 務 : 　中文（國語和廣東話）

服 務 資 源 : 　該會新聞簡報、雙語咨詢人員

該會為會員性組織
入 會 所 需 : 　　20美金年費，學生減半

關 注 之 問 題 : 　平等住房、反種族歧視、青少年問題
、移民權利、經濟發展、社會公正

服 務 對 象 : 　　亞洲及太平洋群島各族裔、老年人、
其他族裔以及猶太族裔

MFT法律服務部

41 Avenue A
New York, NY, 10009

電 話 號 碼 ：　　212-475-8000
電 傳 真 ：　　212-475-1043
聯 系 人 ：　　Wayne G. Hawley　　執 行 主 任

辦 公 時 間 ：　　上午9：30至下午5：30
工 作 人 員 ：　　領 取 薪 金
服 務 地 區 ：　　曼哈頓東區及西部自西34街至110街

服 務 宗 旨 ：　　確 保 貧 困 的 紐 約 市 民 不 因 無 錢 聘 請 律
師 而 被 拒 絕 享 有 平 等 的 法 律 權 益

組 織 概 述 ：　　該 法 律 服 務 部 為 低 收 入 個 人 、 家 庭 和
該 部 所 的 紐 約 市 社 區 組 織 提 供 高 質 量
的 法 律 服 務 。 MFY通 過 執 行 現 行 法 律 ， 提
議 修 改 必 要 的 條 款 以 及 教 育 社 區 等 方 式 保
護 其 客 户 的 權 利 。

雙 語 服 務 ：　　西 班 牙 語 、 中 文

服 務 資 源 ：　　手 冊

該 部 為 非 會 員 性 組 織

關 注 之 問 題 ：　　法 律 事 務 、 住 房 、 無 房 居 住 者 、 社 會
福 利 之 辯 護

服 務 對 象 ：　　曼 哈 頓 之 低 收 入 居 民

뉴욕 아시아계 미국인 협회

Asian American Federation of New York (AAF)

95 Madison Avenue, #1309

New York, NY 10016

전 화:	212-725-3840
팩 스:	212-725-6629
연 락 인:	카오 오 총무
	Cao O, Exec. Director

집무 시간:	월 - 금, 오전 9시 - 오후 5시
직 원:	유급제
대상 지역:	뉴욕 시

단체 목적: 아시아계 미국인의 생활의 질을 향상하기 위한 지역사회내
노력을 지지하며 그에 필요한 지도력과 자원을 양성하는 것이
본 협회의 목적임.

단체 설명: 본 협회는 뉴욕시 아시아계 미국인 지역사회를 대상으로
지역사회내 필요를 담당하는 의료 및 복지기관을 회원단체로
한 비영리 연합체임.

다중언어사용: 중국어, 한국어, 월남어

단체 자원: 소식지, 회원용 회의공간 (비회원의 장소사용은 경우에 따라 가능),
아시아계 미국인에 관한 정보 및 자료, 연수회, 자료열람실.
자료는 영문뿐임.

회원단체유무: 있음.

회원단체 자격: 501(C)(3) 단체들.

안   건: 복지, 투표권, 노인 문제.
회원단체임.

대상 인원: 아시아 및 태평양 열도계 민족.

아시아계 미국인 법적보호 및 교육 재단

Asian American Legal Defense and Education Fund (AALDEF)
99 Hudson Street, 12th Floor
New York, NY 10013

전   화: 212-966-5932
팩   스: 212-966-4303
연 락 인: 마가렡 훵 총무
              Margaret Fung, Exec. Dir.

집무 시간: 오전 9시 30분 - 오후 5시 30분
직   원: 유급제
대상 지역: 뉴욕 시

단체 목적: 법적권리 및 민권

단체 설명: 본 재단은 이민자 권리, 반 아시아계 미국인 폭력, 노동권,
              투표권, 일본계 미국인의 피해 배상 및 환경 정의에 관해
              법정소송, 법적 로비 및 아시아계 미국인 지역사회를 대상
              으로 지역단위 홍보 및 교육을 실시하고 있음.

다중언어사용: 중국어, 한국어, 일본어.

단체 자원: 팜플렛, 입법에 관한 급보 제공, 강연.
회원단체 유무: 있음
회원단체 자격: 본 재단을 지지

안건: 법률, 사회 정의, 투표권, 노동권, 이민자 권리.

대상 인원: 아시아 및 태평양 열도계 민족

Part 3:

.... Resource and technical assistance
people from photographers
to communications
consultants

CAMP KINDERLAND
in the Berkshires

Peace, Justice and the Time of Their Lives !
Full Sports, Arts and Swimming
on Our Own Beautiful Lake.

Emphasis on community,
progressive values, programs
teaching peace, social justice,
multi-cultural and secular
Jewish outlook.

BOYS & GIRLS
Ages 8 - 16
3, 4 or 7 Week Sessions

We make lifelong memories
and friendships; *and* we make
a difference.

Partial Scholarships Available.

Call or write:
CAMP KINDERLAND
1 Union Square West
New York, NY 10003
212-255-6283

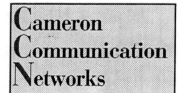

TOM M^cKITTERICK
PHOTOGRAPHER

113 GREENE STREET
NEW YORK CITY
NEW YORK 10012   (212) 431-7697

Jill H. Sheinberg
mediator/attorney

(516) 883-3930   Port Washington, NY

JOAN SWAN
FUNDRAISING AND DEVELOPMENT SERVICES

708 Washington Street, New York, NY 10014
(212) 807-1433

Seven Reasons for Choosing
Ragged Edge Press as Your Printer

1 *W*e provide our customers with accurate, timely estimates at reasonable New York City prices

2 *W*e are excellent trouble shooters, explaining the foreseeable problems of any printing job before it costs you money

3 *W*e handle any size job from a simple, single color business card to the most complex full color brochures and everything in-between

4 *W*e have, for 16 years, provided printing services with care to a myriad of non profit organizations, progressive causes, small businesses, artists, theater groups, and rabble rousers

5 *W*e are obsessive about our printing jobs coming out correctly and on time — the way you want it

6 *W*e gratefully acknowledge the support of our customers and friends in unique ways — our yearly surprise packets are unmatched by any other New York printer

7 *O*ur customers are not merely satisfied, they're ardent fans

102 FULTON STREET, NEW YORK, NY 10038 • 212-962-4488

Jane Hoffer
Freelance Photographer
(212) 663-6404

Electronic Publishing Since 1985
On-Line Marketing & Promotion

Kramer Communications
Felix Kramer, President
310 Riverside Drive, Suite 1519
New York, NY 10025
212/866-4864 FAX 866-5527
INTERNET: felixk@panix.com

Tools to Confront Power with Power

Ray Rogers
Director

51 East 12th Street, 10th floor
New York, NY 10003
(212) 979-8320
FAX (212) 979-1221

Materials for Freedom, Social Justice & Peace

DONNELLY/COLT
PROGRESSIVE RESOURCES

Box 188
Hampton, CT 06427
203-455-9621
Fax 800-553-0006

Kate Donnelly
Clay Colt

Susan Hibbard

594 Broadway • Room 403
New York, NY 10012
Phone: (212) 343-0255 • Fax: (212) 343-2876
E-mail: SGHNGLTF@aol.com

Part 4:

.... Index by Organization
Alphabetically

INDEX BY NAME OF ORGANIZATION

D

E

M

N

O

P

Q

R

S

T

U

V

W

Y

Español/Spanish

Français/French

Creole

Part 5:

.... Index by Issue Areas and
Constituency

INDEX BY ISSUE AND CONSTITUENCY

G

Government Accountability, 2, 5, 7,
16, 26, 27, 29, 40, 41, 61, 62, 65,
68, 75, 82, 86, 107, 121, 122, 144,
145, 147, 158

H

Haitian, 59, 76, 77, 110

Health Care, 5, 7, 9, 16, 20, 23, 27,
32, 42, 50, 51, 54, 58, 66, 77, 116,
119, 121, 143, 153, 159, 160, 163

HIV/AIDS, 1, 2, 5, 9, 16, 20, 22, 24,
42, 50, 63, 65, 71, 73, 78, 80, 84,
88, 98, 100, 103, 111, 115, 125,
126, 127, 153, 159, 164

Homelessness, 2, 6, 7, 11, 17, 19, 20,
22, 32, 34, 39, 40, 42, 49, 51, 54,
65, 66, 72, 79, 80, 81, 87, 90, 105,
108, 116, 125, 130, 135, 147, 151,
153, 163, 164, 165

Housing, 2, 6, 7, 11, 15, 17, 19, 20,
22, 32, 34, 39, 40, 42, 49, 51, 54,
65, 66, 72, 79, 80, 81, 86, 87, 90,
103, 104, 105, 107, 108, 116, 125,
130, 135, 147, 151, 153, 163, 164,
165

Human Rights, 6, 8, 15, 29, 32, 35,
47, 48, 49, 54, 62, 68, 71, 72, 76,
77, 78, 92, 99, 100, 103, 109, 110,
111, 113, 114, 116, 125, 128, 131,
143, 144, 150, 152

Hunger, 11, 49, 66, 116

I

Immigrants' Rights, 9, 14, 15, 30,
32, 36, 39, 48, 55, 73, 76, 77, 84,
90, 99, 110, 111, 126, 137, 141

Int'l Solidarity, 30, 49, 53, 76, 88,
89,,91, 95, 120, 123, 124, 128,
131, 146, 152, 166

Iranian, 48

Irish, 89

J

Jewish, 15, 20, 28, 91

L

Latino/Hispanic, 4, 6, 9, 16, 18, 20,
23, 33, 51, 55, 57, 58, 65, 66, 67,
71, 73, 77, 78, 80, 85, 86, 94, 95,
98, 110, 114, 123, 124, 125, 130,
135, 152, 155, 156, 158, 165

Legal, 3, 9, 10, 14, 32, 33, 77, 78, 80,
81, 86, 108, 111, 164

Lesbian/Gay, 2, 5, 6, 9, 15, 24, 25,
30, 38, 50, 54, 56, 61, 70, 71, 78,
80, 83, 84, 88, 89, 91, 98, 100,
120, 125, 126, 127, 136, 141, 142,
159, 161

Low Income, 34, 82, 91, 108, 117,
145

M

Media, 5, 10, 15, 39, 45, 56, 57, 59,
64, 66, 70, 77, 86, 88, 106, 124,
126, 129, 134, 138, 140, 141, 150,
161, 167

Mental Illness. *See* Disability Rights

Middle Eastern, 10

Multi-Racial, 2, 5, 6, 11, 12, 13, 15,
16, 17, 23, 24, 25, 26, 29, 32, 33,
34, 36, 39, 40, 42, 47, 51, 54, 55,
56, 57, 58, 59, 61, 63, 65, 71, 72,
73, 74, 76, 77, 78, 79, 80, 82, 84,

Part 6:

.... Index by Geographic Scope

INDEX BY ORGANIZATION'S GEOGRAPHIC SCOPE

BRONX
19, 24, 25, 26, 40, 71, 79, 81, 86, 105, 109, 135, 145, 151, 152

Bedford Park	19
South Bronx	26, 37, 86, 132, 145, 154, 216

BROOKLYN
4, 7, 11, 17, 18, 19, 20, 21, 22, 23, 27, 30, 31, 33, 34, 47, 51, 52, 60, 63, 65, 66, 67, 69, 74, 76, 77, 79, 84, 85, 92, 107, 110, 113, 116, 126, 132, 133, 138, 146, 155, 159, 166, 174, 175, 177, 180, 188, 194, 196

Bay Ridge	27
Boro Park	27
Brownsville.	113
Bushwick	113
Park Slope	31, 65, 177
Sunset Park.	27
Williamsburg.	20

CITY-WIDE
1, 2, 3, 4, 5, 6, 7, 8, 9, 10, 11, 12, 13, 14, 15, 16, 17, 18, 22, 23, 25, 28, 29, 30, 32, 33, 34, 36, 38, 39, 40, 41, 42, 43, 44, 45, 47, 48, 49, 50, 54, 55, 56, 57, 58, 59, 60, 61, 62, 63, 64, 65, 66, 67, 68, 69, 71, 72, 74, 75, 76, 80, 81, 83, 84, 86, 87, 88, 89, 90, 91, 92, 93, 94, 95, 98, 99, 100, 104, 105, 107, 108, 110, 111, 112, 114, 115, 116, 117, 118, 119, 120, 121, 122, 123, 125, 126, 127, 128, 129, 130, 131, 133, 134, 137, 138, 141, 142, 143, 144, 150, 151, 152, 154, 155, 156, 159, 161, 163, 164, 166, 167

MANHATTAN
5, 6, 20, 32, 34, 41, 57, 62, 68, 79, 80, 81, 86, 90, 104, 105, 107, 108, 127, 138, 140, 158

Chelsea.	34, 35, 78, 81, 83, 140, 179
Central Harlem	2, 216
Chinatown	12, 15, 90
East Harlem	156, 165
Lower East Side.	14, 15, 20, 73, 79, 90, 102, 103, 124, 127, 164
Upper West Side.	20, 73, 108, 147
Washington Heights.	6, 55, 95
West Harlem	158

NATIONAL
1, 10, 21, 29, 33, 35, 38, 42, 44, 46, 49, 53, 62, 64, 70, 82, 83, 84, 85, 88, 92, 94, 95, 99, 101, 104, 110, 111, 112, 126, 130, 141, 143, 144, 148, 149, 152, 156, 157, 160, 162

QUEENS
3, 13, 28, 42, 95, 107, 129, 136, 137

Long Island City	3, 95, 129

STATEN ISLAND
3, 47, 146, 147, 148

STATEWIDE
61, 106